Disaster Recovery
Planning

G000128662

Titles in the J. Ranade Series on Computer Communications

0-07-054418-2	Sackett	*IBM's Token-Ring Networking Handbook*
0-07-004128-8	Bates	*Disaster Recovery Planning: Networks, Telecommunications, and Data Communications*
0-07-005075-9	Berson	*APPC: Introduction to LU6.2*
0-07-005076-7	Berson	*Client-Server Computing*
0-07-012926-6	Cooper	*Computer and Communications Security*
0-07-016189-5	Dayton	*Telecommunications*
0-07-019022-4	Edmunds	*SAA/LU6.2: Distributed Networks and Applications*
0-07-034242-3	Kessler	*ISDN*
0-07-034243-1	Kessler/Train	*Metropolitan Area Networks: Concepts, Standards, and Service*

Other Related Titles

0-07-051144-6	Ranade/Sackett	*Introduction to SNA Networking: A Guide for Using VTAM/NCP*
0-07-051143-8	Ranade/Sackett	*Advanced SNA Networking: A Professional's Guide to VTAM/NCP*
0-07-033727-6	Kapoor	*SNA: Architecture, Protocols, and Implementation*
0-07-005553-X	Black	*TCP/IP and Related Protocols*
0-07-005554-8	Black	*Network Management Standards: SNMP, CMOT, and OSI*
0-07-021625-8	Fortier	*Handbook of LAN Technology, Second Edition*

Disaster Recovery Planning

Networks, Telecommunications, and Data Communications

Regis J. Bates, Jr.

McGraw-Hill, Inc.

New York   St. Louis   San Francisco   Auckland   Bogotá
Caracas   Lisbon   London   Madrid   Mexico   Milan
Montreal   New Delhi   Paris   San Juan   São Paulo
Singapore   Sydney   Tokyo   Toronto

DISASTER RECOVERY PLANNING
INTERNATIONAL EDITION 1992

Exclusive rights by McGraw-Hill Book Co.- Singapore for
manufacture and export. This book cannot be re-exported from the
country to which it is consigned by McGraw-Hill.

1 2 3 4 5 6 7 8 9 0 CMO UP 9 7 6 5 4 3 2

Copyright © 1992 by McGraw-Hill, Inc. All rights reserved. Except
as permitted under the United States Copyright Act of 1976, no
part of this publication may be reproduced or distributed in any
form or by any means, or stored in a data base or retrieval
system, without the prior written permission of the publisher.

Library of Congress Cataloging-in-Publication Data

Bates, Regis J.
  Disaster recovery planning : networks, telecommunications, and
data communications/Regis J. Bates, Jr
     p.   cm-(McGraw-Hill series on computer communications)
  Includes index.
  ISBN 0-07-004128-8
  1. Telecommunication systems-Security measures-Planning.
2. Disaster relief-Planning.   I. Title   II. Series.
TK5102.5.B344   1991
363.3′48-dc20   91-40560
                                         CIP

ISBN 0-07-004128-8

The sponsoring editor for this book was Jerry Papke, and the
production supervisor was Donald F. Schmidt. It was set in Century
Schoolbook by North Market Street Graphics.

TRADEMARKS

Microsoft Word is a registered trademark of Microsoft Corporation.
Microsoft Excel is a registered trademark of Microsoft Corporation.
WP is a registered trademark of Word Perfect Corporation.
Lotus 1-2-3 is a registered trademark of Lotus Development Corporation.
Oracle is a registered trademark of Oracle Corporation.
Harvard Graphics is a registered trademark of Software Publishing
    Corporation.
Harvard Project Mgr & Word Processor are registered trademarks of
    Software Publishing Corporation.
VAXII/780 is a registered trademark of Digital Equipment Corporation.
Ethernet is a registered trademark of Xerox Corporation, Intel
    Corporation, and Digital Corporation.
Timeline is a registered trademark of Symantec Corporation.
TPGMGR is a registered trademark of Oracel Corporation.
TRPS is a registered trademark of CHI/COR Information
    Management, Inc.

Not for re-sale in Australia, Canada, Europe, Japan, the United
Kingdom and the United States. Export sale may be made only by or with
the express consent of the publisher.

When ordering this title, use ISBN 0-07-112966-9

Printed in Singapore

This book is dedicated to my loving wife, Gabriele, who has always been my strength and spirit. Without her to stand by me, this book would still be a dream unfulfilled.

Contents

List of Figures   xi
List of Tables   xiii
Preface   xv

Chapter 1. Introduction   1

   1.1   Introduction   1
   1.2   Why Do We Have to Plan at All?   2
          1.2.1   What is disaster recovery planning?   4
          1.2.2   What is involved in disaster recovery planning?   6
          1.2.3   What business are you in?   10
   1.3   Historical Events   11
          1.3.1   The Hinsdale fire   11
                  1.3.1.1   Factors leading up to the Hinsdale fire   12
          1.3.2   Hurricane Hugo   14
          1.3.3   The San Francisco earthquake   15
          1.3.4   The quake that never happened   16
          1.3.5   The Penn Mutual fire   16
   1.4   Other Disasters Affecting Telecommunications   17
          1.4.1   AT&T's network   17
          1.4.2   Illinois Bell   18
          1.4.3   The Consolidated Edison fire   18

Chapter 2. Getting Started?   21

   2.1   The Preliminary Plan   21
          2.1.1   Historical facts   21
   2.2   Networking with Others   23
   2.3   Do Your Homework   25
   2.4   What About That All-Important Presentation?   26

Chapter 3. The Planning Process   29

   3.1   Presenting the Plan to Management   29
          3.1.1   Gathering the facts   29
          3.1.2   The business impact analysis   31
          3.1.3   Example of a loss   31
          3.1.4   Additional items   33
   3.2   Options in Developing Your Plan   35

Chapter 4. Recruiting the Team   37

4.1   Recruiting the Team   37
4.2   Just Who Should You Involve on the Team?   38
4.3   Build an Awareness   40
4.4   Staffing Issues   41
    4.4.1   Where do you get the people?   41
    4.4.2   How do you get them?   42
    4.4.3   What departments should the team be from?   42
4.5   Building the Hype!   43
4.6   Assigning the Tasks and Following Up   45
4.7   Logistics   47

Chapter 5. The Inventory Process   49

5.1   Conducting the Inventory   49
    5.1.1   Who should be involved in the inventory process?   49
5.2   What Should Be Inventoried?   50
    5.2.1   Assessing the existing equipment   50
    5.2.2   Mapping out the internal facilities   55
    5.2.3   Mapping the external facilities   55
    5.2.4   Mapping out the carrier-to-carrier handoff   58
5.3   Working with Your Carriers   59
5.4   Working with Your Vendors   60
5.5   What About Distributors?   62
5.6   Assessing Your Risk Points   63

Chapter 6. Looking at the Alternatives   73

6.1   Looking at the Alternatives   73
6.2   Technologies Available   74
6.3   Cable Television (CATV) Systems   74
6.4   Cellular Radio   77
6.5   Microwave Radio   80
6.6   Satellite and Very Small Aperture Terminal (VSAT)   83
6.7   Two-way Radio   85
6.8   Fiber Optics   86
6.9   Infrared   90
6.10   Alternate Access Carriers   90
6.11   Shared Services with Other Users   93
6.12   Reconfigure or Reroute What You Have   94
6.13   Use Existing Types of Services   96
6.14   Network Hot Sites   98

Chapter 7. Vendor and Carrier Strategies   103

7.1   Vendor and Carrier Strategies   103
    7.1.1   Vendors   103
7.2   Private Branch Exchange (PBX) Vendors   104
7.3   Modem and Mux Vendors   107

7.4	Computer Manufacturers	107
7.5	Data Processing Hot Site Vendors	108
7.6	Carriers	110
	7.6.1 Local Exchange Carriers (LECs)	110
	7.6.2 Interexchange vendors	111
	7.6.2.1 Route diversity rings	112
	7.6.2.2 Dual-fed rings	113
	7.6.2.3 Reconfigurable rings	113
	7.6.3 Other exchange carriers	113
	7.6.3.1 Cable diversity	114
	7.6.3.2 Bundle diversity	114
	7.6.3.3 Count diversity	114
	7.6.3.4 Right-of-way diversity	114
	7.6.3.5 Adjacency diversity	114
	7.6.3.6 Adjacent innerduct	114
	7.6.4 When is a diverse route not a diverse route?	114
	7.6.5 Independents	115

Chapter 8. Networks and Topologies 117

8.1	Networks and Topologies	117
	8.1.1 Local Area Networks	117
	8.1.2 Wide Area Networks	117
	8.1.3 Metropolitan Area Networks	117
	8.1.4 Electronic Tandem Network (ETN)/ Electronic Switched Network (ESN)	118
8.2	Local Area Networks (LANs)	118
	8.2.1 Media	118
	8.2.2 Equipment	118
8.3	Metropolitan Area Networks (MANs)	119
	8.3.1 Media	120
	8.3.2 Equipment	120
8.4	Wide Area Networks (WANs)	120
	8.4.1 Media	121
	8.4.2 Equipment	121
8.5	Bandwidths	122
8.6	Other Networks (ETN/ESN)	122
	8.6.1 Media	123
	8.6.2 Equipment	123
8.7	Risks	124

Chapter 9. The Plan: Tying It All Together 127

9.1	Disaster Recovery and Restoration Plan	127
9.2	Section I: Administrative Statement	129
9.3	Section II: The Action Plan	130
9.4	Section III: Testing	131
9.5	Section IV: Maintenance	132
9.6	Section V: Training	133
9.7	Section VI: Appendices	134

x   Contents

Appendix A. Alternate Site Vendors   135

Appendix B. Uninterrupted Power System Vendors   143

**Appendix C. Satellite and Very Small Aperture Terminal
(VSAT) Vendors**   145

Appendix D. Disaster Recovery Planning Software Vendors   147

Appendix E. Disaster Recovery Related Magazines   149

Glossary   151
Index   155

List of Figures

CHAPTER 2

2.1	What constitutes a disaster?	22
2.2	Organizing for disaster recovery.	25
2.3	The business impact analysis.	27

CHAPTER 4

4.1	Working committee plan development.	38
4.2	MIS and telecom recovery team.	39

CHAPTER 5

5.1	Protect cable facilities at the entrance to the building.	52
5.2	Protecting the telecommunications environment.	53
5.3	Riser, closet, and cable vault diversity.	56
5.4	Look for single points of failure within your organization.	57
5.5	Feeds to two COs provide protection in the event of backhoe fade.	59
5.6	Vendor replacement systems on wheels.	61

CHAPTER 6

6.1	Use CATV as an alternate access supplier.	76
6.2	The cellular radio/telephone network.	79
6.3	Private microwave.	82
6.4	Satellite communications.	85
6.5	Hubbing system in the telephone company network.	87
6.6	Ring architecture using fiber optics in networks.	89
6.7	Infrared communications.	91
6.8	Alternate access carriers.	91
6.9	Sharing network resources through a cooperative network (CO-Net).	94

6.10   Reconfigure what you have: existing networks.   96
6.11   Reconfigure what you have: revised network with
       fractional T1.   97
6.12   Use 56/64 Kbps dial backup services in the event
       of a line/network failure.   98
6.13   Use T1 to back up 9.6/56 Kbps data services.   99
6.14   Use V.32 modem to back up DDS at 56 Kbps.   100
6.15   Dial backup for DataComm using modem pooling.   101

CHAPTER 7

7.1   Diverse routing to IXC through two different central
       offices (COs).   112

CHAPTER 8

8.1   Telecommunications disasters and disruptions causes. 125

CHAPTER 9

9.1   Sequence of steps necessary to get back into
       business after an event/disaster occurs.   128

List of Tables

1.1   Steps to Help You Get Started   10
3.1   The Business Impact of a Disaster   31
3.2   Case Example of a Loss After Disaster   32
5.1   Inventory of Equipment   54
8.1   Summary of Network, Topologies, and Capacities   122
8.2   Summary of Bandwidths of the Various Media
       Being Used   123

Preface

Planning for disasters is a new phenomenon in the telecommunications world. In the past three years, many companies who took the subject of disasters for granted have since learned that the use of telecommunications is critical to the successful completion of their objectives. Many of these firms had to react to disasters in their world without the benefit of having a plan in place. Unfortunately, some have ceased to exist because of the inability to get back into business, and to reestablish their communications links to the rest of the world in an expedient manner.

We all take the telecommunications network for granted. Justifiably so. We have the best and most sophisticated network in the world. However, many feelings of false security prevail in our industry today. We feel that the carriers and vendors are prepared to deal with our problems immediately, if something should happen to the network, the facilities, or the equipment. Therein lies the problem! We are responsible for the health of our networks. Others are contributors to this environment, but cannot be solely responsible.

The purpose of this book is not to scare the reader into a frenzy, but to point out the risks, the possible solutions, and, foremost, the preventative steps that can be taken. The author would rather see an organization prevent a disaster than have to react to one. However, should the inevitable happen, this book will try to point out ways of recovering from a disaster. Moreover, the development and testing of a plan must be realistic. We cannot expect our organizations to fund the most elaborate plan in the industry and break the bank. Thus, we must look for inexpensive solutions to protect the very livelihood of our organization.

Regis J. Bates, Jr.

1

Introduction

1.1 INTRODUCTION

The use of the words "disaster" and "recovery" implies that everyone is destined to live through a disaster in his or her lifetime and that the ability to overcome the disaster, or *recover from it,* depends on the ability of an organization to pull its resources together in a logical fashion, dole out responsibilities to designated teams, and ultimately put all the pieces back together. Unfortunately, many organizations do not have a propensity to deal with the subject in just that manner. They wait until a disaster strikes; then they set out to recover from it. This wastes valuable time and causes undue stress on their staffs. Since no one has a set of rules by which to recover from this event, time is wasted in the attempt to coordinate the activities of several individuals (or teams) at the same time. The demands on management and staff alike prolong the effects of the disaster to unacceptable levels. This can cause losses of business and revenues at a time when they are needed most. Companies can no longer sustain their operations without the use of some form of communication. Their day-to-day operations depend on the use of networks, telecommunications, and data communications services. From the simple phone call (to place or receive an order) to the interconnection of multiple networks (local area, wide area, etc.) to the ability to move information (data) across networks, businesses have become critically dependent on the use of

telecommunications capabilities. Without networks to process information, operations get thrown into utter chaos. The functions of businesses literally grind to a halt. How soon these processes of functional
death take place depends on the degree of delay that can be tolerated.
For most companies this can occur within 72 hours, which really is not
that long. The objective is to be back in service (degraded at best) as
soon as possible, but within 72 hours.

1.2 WHY DO WE HAVE TO PLAN AT ALL?

There has been much ado about planning for and preventing disasters
in telecommunications networks and facilities over the past couple of
years. The hot button in the telecommunications industry, as well as
the user population these days, is the presence or absence of a disaster
recovery plan. (A more desirable term would be "business resumption
plan.")

Why all the emphasis now, when this was taken for granted for
years? Let's take a look at just what happened to spur the interest to
such a magnitude. A good starting point is that fateful day in May 1988.

1. On May 8, 1988, a historical event took place in Hinsdale, Illinois
   when the Central Office (CO) burned down, causing total disruption
   of service to over 500,000 customers being served by or through this
   CO.

   Although this event started the whole chain of events, there have
   been other significant events of equal importance which have
   affected our telecommunications facilities and networks. The
   Hinsdale fire, although old news, brought to light that even the cor-
   nerposts of our networks and facilities are exposed to disruption.
   Users were living in a dream world, thinking they were protected
   from catastrophic losses because the Local Exchange Carriers
   (LECs) had designed all the necessary precautions to prevent situations of this magnitude. No one doubts that the LECs have done a
   remarkable job of protecting their assets, and in turn minimized the
   risk of exposure for the end user. However, an element of risk exists
   in *any* system, that being *human intervention,* which can override
   any and all safeguards put in place.

   Hinsdale was only the start. This event will be covered in greater
   detail later. However, there were other events in the chain causing
   equal concern on the part of LECs, InterExchange Carriers, (IXCs),
   and users alike, such as:

2. In September 1989, Hurricane Hugo tore through the coastal city of
   Charleston, South Carolina, leaving a path of destruction behind it.

Here was a natural disaster which, given the nature of the storm and the course it was traveling, should have stayed at sea and missed land. Yet no one can predict Mother Nature's intentions to such a degree of accuracy that all will go according to plan. Hugo caused major disruptions to telecommunications, not from the loss of communications facilities, but from the loss of power, which was the major cause of downtime.

3. In October 1989, a major earthquake in the San Francisco, California area rocked the country with the speed and devastation it caused. Once again, the loss of communications was isolated to causes other than COs going down. The bulk of the disruptions were the result of cables being ripped from their connection points and commercial power being lost.

4. Throughout 1989, other natural disasters caused the loss of communications services. These events included tornadoes, floods, other hurricanes, and extreme cold temperatures.

5. In January 1990, American Telephone and Telegraph (AT&T) experienced a software glitch which severely impaired the ability of users to complete calls across AT&T's network. Because this was software related, the fear of a major computer virus slipping into the network ran rampant.

6. In October 1990, Illinois Bell suffered a major cable cut in the network. Financial houses closed and radar services at the local airports were disrupted, causing concern among all.

7. On June 26, 1991, glitches in the sophisticated equipment (computer systems software) led to major outages in both Washington, D.C., and Los Angeles, California. The extent of the outages was that over nine million lines were impaired, affecting local services and cellular communications.

    The problem resided in the Signaling System Seven (SS7) software which triggered a chain reaction across the network. Some of the business and government agencies were literally paralyzed for the duration of the problem, being restricted from accessing local services.

    In Washington, D.C., C&P Telephone Company's outages lasted approximately seven hours and affected close to 90 percent of the COs in Maryland, Washington, and the Virginias. By contrast, the Los Angeles, California problem was less severe, lasting only two-and-a-half to three hours and affecting only 50 COs. Also, the problem was isolated to a far smaller area.

    Both problems were attributed to glitches in the SS7 software at the Signal Transfer Points (STPs) provided by the same vendor.

While the problems were being investigated, rumors of viruses and hackers ran rampant. The country was in panic over the potential threat of this sort.

There is some similarity between the Washington, D.C. and Los Angeles, California problems and AT&T's problem in January 1990. This merely underscores the increasing complexity of our computerized communications facilities and networks. Furthermore, it reinforces our need to be prepared for inevitable network crises.

How can we prepare for a major telephone company problem? The more sophisticated the networks get, the greater the risks of and the more vulnerable we are to network outages.

8. Another form of disaster is the potential for major losses in long distance charges through "toll fraud." With the openness of our systems through Remote Access and Direct Inward Systems Access (DISA), we have avenues of penetration into our networks, leaving exposures high. The industry is experiencing record numbers of unauthorized usage of systems and services as hackers break through trivial password protection schemes and place long distance calls both domestically and internationally, leaving end user companies holding the tabs. Industry experts are estimating losses in billions of dollars per year, and climbing.

It would appear that the cards are stacked against users and carriers alike where natural causes are concerned. Yet other events occurred that were not sensational enough to draw press coverage, leaving them unreported. Some of the other incidents included fires, power losses, cable cuts, vandalism, and viruses.

1.2.1   What is disaster recovery planning?

Disaster recovery planning is a process to help the business recover from a disaster quickly. The loss of communications facilities and networks will seriously impair the organization's ability to perform its primary purpose. When looking at the planning process, the primary goals are to:

1. First and foremost, *protect human life.* The organization is responsible for the safeguarding of life. Telecommunications is critical in many cases after a disaster to help save lives and to treat the injured. Thus, a plan must be developed to provide for the quick reestablishment of communications after an unplanned outage.

2. *Minimize the impact on the business,* which results from the loss of the communications capability. Today's organizations depend heav-

ily on the ability to move information quickly and reliably. The disruption of service can cause severe consequential damage to the business. Many small businesses were financially crippled after extended outages of their communications, with some being forced to close their businesses totally.

3. Provide a detailed *set of procedures* to follow when a disaster occurs. In most cases, the presence of the plan and the orderly flow of instructions to follow prevents a disruption from escalating into a disaster (or catastrophe). Many organizations experiencing problems created more severe consequences, since they did not have a plan in place to deal with the situation. The lack of a plan led to extended periods of downtime, caused chaos in the environment, and caused the loss of customer and employee confidence in the organization. This loss of customer confidence may lead to the loss of customers! The loss of employee confidence may lead to the need to replace valuable workers, who leave as a result of their feelings of insecurity or of their lives being at risk.

4. *Look at things a whole new way.* The planning process allows the user to take a more stringent look at the environment. All too often, networks, facilities, and systems are designed around technological considerations. By reviewing policies and procedures, risk points, and operational considerations, the end user can reinforce the weak areas. Look at your environment with a different perspective; not a telecommunications one, but a safety and security one. You may be surprised at just what you discover! In many cases, potential risks and problems build up over time. Since you see the area on a regular basis, the risks go unnoticed. You tend to overlook the problems, and evolution from a secure and safe environment to a risky one gradually takes place.

5. *Develop a protection policy against internal and external threats.* Opportunities exist for employees who are disgruntled or careless, who violate smoking regulations, etc., to cause disruptions to communications. External factors can also create the need to react. Think of all the construction going on in every major city across the country. Now think of all the ensuing cable cuts. Other areas in facilities management and provisions are equally affected by these external conditions.

So, the emphasis has shifted from one of passivity, when dealing with the integrity and survivability of our networks and facilities, to one of intent concern. Everyone is jumping on the telecommunications bandwagon.

For now, though, let's look at what the definition of disaster recovery for networks, telecommunications, and data communications is all about. Looking at the words individually, they can be defined as:

Disaster: accident, catastrophe, tragedy, or emergency

Recovery: heal, retrieve, regain

Putting the words together in some semblance of order, you would arrive at a definition of disaster recovery that looks like this:

A plan to heal and retrieve the telecommunications networks and facilities after a catastrophic loss, until such a time that you can reconstruct and reestablish the systems to a form of normalcy, which existed prior to the disaster.

Stated another way:

An organization's ability to continue its day-to-day operations, despite an occurrence of a catastrophic nature, through a series of coordinated and preplanned activities with the awareness and endorsement of senior management. It is the informal insurance policy to provide business perpetuity through an attitude that telecommunications is a critical resource to the organization's livelihood.

This thought process states that telecommunications is a critical resource for the organization's livelihood. More and more companies, firms, and government organizations are becoming aware of the importance of telecommunications in their everyday lives. Just try to conduct your activities without the use of a phone, fax, modem, etc. for one day, and see how well you do!

1.2.2 What is involved in disaster recovery planning?

For those in the telecommunications field (supplier, reseller, or user), it is the preplanning steps which can be taken that prevent utter chaos in your organization when some event occurs. It is *preventative* in nature, a thought process and an attitude shift from the days of false security.

To use a phrase from the Boy Scouts, "Be prepared." We could say it is the process of taking a serious look at the equipment, facilities, environmental, and external issues that surround your operation. Once you decide to take that serious look at your organization, you must be prepared to eliminate risk or exposure points. This also means that you should look at everything from a different perspective. To assume everything has been designed and built with systems and network integrity in mind would be a fallacy. View the operation in light of the areas that may still be subject to failure and/or penetration from outside influences.

This hard-look approach will include a willingness to put aside self-protecting interests. As the architects of the networks or facilities, you may have a tendency to be somewhat protective, and therefore not recognize any potential dangers. It may be difficult to go back to management and ask for additional funding or resources to reinforce or redesign that system which recently cost thousands or millions to install. Yet, if the goal is truly to protect the organization's livelihood, then face reality. There may still be some flaws in the armor!

If you already have a disaster recovery plan in effect, then you may well be able to modify it slightly. Look at new ways of reinforcing the plan. Recognize the need to enforce policies and procedures, and put additional penalties in place to deal with violations and infractions.

If, however, you have no plan in place, then you need to understand the risks and the options available to you. Look within your organization to determine if another department already has a contingency plan in place, which you can use as either:

1. *A model.* Since the existing plan probably was accepted by senior management, you will be able to use a pre-approved format that management will accept.

2. *A vehicle to incorporate yours into.* Why reinvent the wheel if you can get away with incorporating a new piece into an existing plan? This will serve as a reminder to update on a continual basis, since, hopefully, the existing plan is on a scheduled review and update cycle. You will merely be a recipient of the notices when it is time to update.

3. *A tool to help create an awareness* that networks, telecommunications, and data communications are critical and need to be protected. *Visibility* will be a key factor in your approach to selling your plan.

4. *A means by which you can recruit other user departments and external sources to assist you in developing the plan.* Typically, a telecommunications function is understaffed. All too often, the function serves as a part-time or additional duty for an administrative manager. Thus, when you develop a plan, gaining acceptance from users who are willing to commit resources in the event of a disaster will be crucial. Use whatever resources you can.

Some of the key areas where you may look for existing plans are:

- Management Information Services (MIS) Department
- Facilities Department
- Internal Audit
- Operations Department

Many of these departments probably have a plan of some sort, but may not have considered the need for telecommunications in their plan. So, using the exposure wisely can go a long way in selling and developing the plan.

Before you can start this whole process, certain aspects must be considered. For now, they are listed below.

1. Develop a clear understanding of your business. Just what business are you in? Oftentimes, telecommunications managers state that they are in the telecommunications business. This may be true in some cases, but a closer look at their responsibilities would reveal that they manage and provide a utilitarian function to the business entities. They are actually in the business that their organization is chartered in (i.e., the manufacture of pharmaceuticals, the transportation business, or the development and sale of widgets). Only when this recognition is achieved can you go about protecting the needs of your organization's business.

2. Prepare a preliminary plan to present to your management. Try to get their approval to proceed with the plan development prior to investing time and money into it. Too often, others have attempted to develop a plan in a vacuum, only to be totally demoralized when their managements were "slightly less than enthusiastic." So, work this issue into the goals of the department or the entire organization.

3. Conduct a detailed inventory of all your systems, networks, and facilities. To accomplish this, consider the use of outside resources. If you are an LEC, you will have to deal with interdepartmental issues, as well as dealing with IXCs. As an IXC, the plan will deal with LECs, customers, and other IXCs. As an end-user, the plethora of vendors and carriers who must be dealt with can be overwhelming.

4. Understand the financial impact of the development and implementation of a plan. Contrast this cost to the potential financial devastation caused by the lack of a plan. Just how long could your organization survive without the use of networks, telecommunications, and data communications? The answer is not one that you can generate. This is the responsibility of the operational and financial management in your organization. However, if you ask them this question, you may be surprised that they do not know. Once they analyze the answer to this question, shock may set in based on the answer. Typically, an organization dependent on the use of communications to conduct the day-to-day business (and what organization is not dependent on these technologies?) will be in serious trouble after a few days!

5. Legal consequences must be considered when conducting your research (i.e., the potential for lawsuits if a disaster occurs and you are not properly prepared to deal with the situation). This can come from a number of different avenues.

   - Shareholders could sue for compensation for the lack of "due diligence" or prudence, which is the responsibility of senior management of the organization.

   - Financial institutions are required, by law, to have a plan in place to recover from a disaster within six hours. If the plan does not exist, they face the threat of being "shut down" by the regulators. Worse yet, they face catastrophic losses of mammoth proportions without a plan in place.

   - Customers with contracts to receive goods and services on specific dates which are jeopardized by a disaster could have subsequent nonperformance remedies or consequential damage claims. The shift to "just in time" manufacturing exposes many companies to suits whenever a disruption occurs in the normal production process.

6. Options that are available today. The use of alternative technologies or services on the market will help minimize investment costs. Many options exist to protect and reconfigure your networks, telecommunications, and data communications. However, the need to maintain an open mind while reviewing these alternatives is paramount. Remember to keep all options open rather than opting for a single technical solution or service.

7. Environmental issues within your organization are of equal importance. These include:

   - Physical security (or lack thereof)
   - Space conditioning (power, lights, air conditioning)
   - Fire detection/suppression systems
   - External conditions such as construction

8. The strengths and limitations of your human resources are critical. Detailed lists of the people issues are required, which can be compiled by the Human Resources Department, such as:

   - Physical needs (medical, emotional, spiritual)
   - Logistical problems (space and basic human needs)
   - Emotional problems and limitations (caused by stress, etc.)
   - Accessibility
   - Commitment

Table 1.1 is a summary of what was outlined above and a checksheet for your positive action. The steps necessary to get you started in the planning process are critical.

1.2.3 What business are you in?

Most users get so caught up with providing telecommunications goods and services to their organizations that they forget just what business they are in. The primary business of your organization must be clearly understood before you can address disaster recovery and restoration needs.

You should be aware of what the organization's business plans are, so that you can provide some form of recovery services in support of the corporate charter on both a tactical and a strategic basis. If you lose sight of your users' business needs (whether they are business, municipal, government, or telecommunications providers), then odds are your business continuation and resumption plans will be misdirected on some tangent other than the rest of the organization. That would be a critical shortcoming for the organization, since this disparity in plan-

TABLE 1.1 Steps To Help You Get Started	
Priority	Steps To Be Taken
1.	Make a decision to consider disaster recovery
2.	Understand your business
3.	Prepare a preliminary plan for management
4.	Conduct a detailed inventory of internal systems
5.	Conduct a detailed inventory of facilities
6.	Use outside resources to conduct inventories of external facilities
7.	Conduct a business impact analysis
8.	Consider the legal consequences of no plan
9.	Look at all the options available to you
10.	Recruit assistance from internal organizations
11.	Check security and environmental conditions
12.	Seek a mentor
13.	Present the preliminary plan to management
14.	Prepare a realistic budget
15.	Expect approval
16.	Handle questions proactively
17.	Stay on target and within budget

ning and direction would cause severe limitations in the conduct of business, and thereby jeopardize the livelihood and survivability of the company.

Therefore, you must get involved with your clients, who are the internal or external users of your services. No matter what the organizational structure or charter, you must understand their business needs. You can usually get their cooperation by sending out a series of questionnaires on a fact-finding basis. Outline the required information necessary to provide some *degraded* service in the event of a disaster. In most cases, you will receive an expeditious reply; in the event that you do not, be persistent. It is your responsibility to provide the telecommunications services to the organization, and you cannot ignore this need.

1.3   HISTORICAL EVENTS

These days, a considerable amount of emphasis on and awareness of the need for contingency plans exists. Everyone is acutely aware of the problems affecting telecommunications and the business impacts of the events over the past two years. A realization that nothing is secure has settled in. Remarkably, the issues of the Hinsdale fire have caused panic in the industry, while the LECs, IXCs, and Other Common Carriers (OCCs) have all been scurrying around trying to reinforce their networks and systems so that a repeat of the Hinsdale situation will not happen. They have spent a considerable amount of money and dedicated resources to find their exposure and correct the problem. We have all learned from this event, no matter how tragic, that it was a boon to providers and users alike. The industry had become lax, thinking that this would not happen. Yet destiny had a few things to say about that.

Let's look at the chain of events leading up to this monumental day in the industry from an educational and lessons-learned basis only. The intent of this book is not to beat up or criticize the Bell Operating, Independent Operating, InterExchange, or other companies. More realistically, the purpose is an educational one, a way to learn from the past, so that prevention in the future can prevail.

1.3.1   The Hinsdale fire

Before totally delving into this situation, understand that there were other CO fires, some affecting more lines than Hinsdale. However, the significance of this one was its positioning in the network as a major gateway for local, long distance, fiber, and cellular services. The most notable fires in COs were:

1975   New York City, Second Avenue, which affected 170,000 lines. However, the outages were isolated to mostly one geographic area, and did not affect other services.

1987   New York City, Bushwick, which affected 41,000 lines. Equally as large as the Hinsdale CO, but once again kept to a local level geographically.

1988   Hinsdale, Illinois, the one everyone has heard about because it was recent, and although it only affected 42,000 lines, it affected in excess of 500,000 customers. It was a major gateway for all services and affected multiple other COs, both Bell and Independent Telephone Companies.

Table 1.2 summarizes these outages and the major impact on multiple users.

1.3.1.1 Factors leading up to the Hinsdale fire

Several months before the fire occurred, a subcontractor was performing some cable mining in the CO to relieve congestion in the cable trays. During this process, the subcontractor inadvertently damaged some armor-shielded electrical cabling (this was a Direct Current [DC] power line), which went undetected. As a result, the stage was set for a future disaster.

On May 8, 1988, there were several severe electrical storms brewing around the area. A series of alarms from several different COs was sent back to a remote monitoring office. Hinsdale is an unattended

TABLE 1.2 Major Events in Telecommunications			
Year	Place	Type event	Impact
1975	New York	Central Office fire	170,000 lines affected
1987	New York	Central Office fire	41,000 lines affected
1988	Hinsdale	Central Office fire	42,000 lines affected, 500,000 customers affected
1990	Country-wide	Cable cuts	Major user and network impacts

office. Thinking the alarms were caused by the lightning activity, the technician cleared the alarms and ignored the conditions. Additional alarms poured into the monitoring office. It was not until a second alarm came in that the technician finally called the dispatch supervisor. The supervisor then dispatched a technician to Hinsdale CO. Unfortunately, it was too late; a fire was roaring. Telephone service was already affected. By the time the technician got to the CO, there was no phone service. The technician had to flag down a passing motorist and ask him to report the fire to the local fire department.

Once the fire department personnel arrived, they immediately took control of the building and had the Bell technician leave. Firemen went around the office trying to power down the equipment. Unaware of the design of a CO, they turned off the commercial power to various pieces of equipment, but the backup system automatically activated and reenergized the systems. Therefore, the extinguishing of flames was impeded by the backup power systems, thus delaying the process. After the initial delays of powering off the equipment, the firemen began to use their next tool to control the fire. They started their hoses to defeat the flames. However, when water is poured on electrical and electronic equipment, it has a devastating effect.

To compound these problems further, the water mixed with the toxic fumes, and the chemicals from the burning polyvinylchloride (PVC) cable created hydrochloric acid which became airborne in mist form, moving throughout the CO, dripping on and destroying the electronic equipment.

Although this may sound like a problem, which it was, it served as a useful reminder for everyone to reevaluate the systems and processes in their environments. Had this not occurred, several major points of exposure would still exist in networks and COs. Some valuable lessons were learned from this tragic fire from which all can benefit. Each of the problems outlined in this disaster has provided a series of action items to work with in protecting systems and facilities.

- Do you have an unattended operation during certain hours of the day, week, etc.?

- What procedures exist if an alarm comes in? Do the recipients of the alarm know what to do first?

- Do you have sufficient protection in the event of a fire? What damages can be sustained if the suppression systems get activated?

- Do you test and train on these systems regularly?

These are the basic questions that may spur other thoughts as you review your specific site situations.

1.3.2 Hurricane Hugo

On that warm September 21, 1989, the City of Charleston, South Carolina and all of its residents had more to think about than the summer day and all of its splendor. A hurricane dubbed "Hugo" was on the way, and threatened to wreak havoc on the three-hundred-year-old city.

The population of Charleston had an advantage, though. They were warned well in advance of the approaching monster. Having heard of the destruction caused in the Caribbean by Hugo, the emergency crews were in position to react. Provisions were made for emergency repair parts to be on hand. Hugo came through rather quickly, but was followed by over nine inches of rain, which caused severe flooding in addition to the damage caused by the wind. Hundreds of homes and businesses were lost, trees were toppled like match sticks, and telephone and electric services were virtually nonexistent. Yet the pre-planning that went into the disaster recovery plans addressed the provisions needed to deal with Hugo's wrath. It took seventeen days to restore total electric and telephone service to the area. This was due in part to the plan, and in part to the efforts of workers who pulled together working around the clock. Heroes emerge whenever a disaster strikes. South Carolina had its share of superhuman efforts by both individuals and organizations.

The cost to insurance companies for Hugo-related losses was between $3.9 and $4 billion, a significant amount for anyone's imagination. Not all of this was in Charleston; it included the Caribbean, North Carolina, South Carolina, Virginia, and Georgia.

Many of the damages were to buildings, trees, and downed utility poles. The phone service was disrupted due to lack of power or the inability to replenish the diesel fuel for the generators used to power the COs, as well as other communications systems (i.e., cellular networks). Most of the telephone company lines are buried. Therefore, the damage was far less than expected. Isolated instances were reported of damaged Private Branch Exchanges (PBXs) or Telephone Systems and computer systems at user locations, but the most prevalent problem was still from the loss of power. An additional lesson learned was in the area of security. Many of the portable power generators used to restore telephone services were subject to theft. Since power was a bigger issue, many independents and homeowners stole the generators for their own personal use. This caused further delays in restoring services to the masses. At one point, things were so bad that armed guards were used to protect the portable generators. This was not one of the great moments in the history of telecommunications!

1.3.3   The San Francisco earthquake

As the country was preparing to watch the World Series baseball game in Oakland, California, the earth began to "rumble" beneath the city of San Francisco and the surrounding communities. It was 5:04 p.m., October 17, 1989, and a new disaster was in the making. This was one of the factors which was destined to end 1989 as the worst on record for disasters. Some 29 natural disasters struck the country in 1989, bringing a new sense of awareness to the words "disaster recovery and contingency planning."

The quake, registering 7.1 on the Richter scale, lasted for a mere 15 seconds, yet the destruction was in the billions of dollars. The phones were in trouble, since a lot of the damage was caused from cables being ripped out of the mounting blocks and/or being cut. This was coupled with losses of power in the area. However, the local COs and the long-distance networks survived. Cellular services were up and running, except the demand and peak load caused severe blockages. Interestingly, within an hour after the quake, AT&T's network was processing one million calls every five minutes.

The Telecommunications Priority Restoral Services (TPRS), a systematic process of shedding loads at the local COs, can be implemented after a disaster of this nature, returning services on a priority basis to:

- Agencies dealing with national defense

- Fire departments

- Police

- Health care facilities, hospitals, etc.,

- Municipal governments, airports, etc.

As you can see, businesses and residences are pretty well down the priority list in this example. So, users have to plan what to do in the event of similar occurrences. An additional thought: telephone calls to areas that still had service were blocked on an intra-lata (local) basis, yet out-of-state calls were allowed more freely. This allowed for the quick connection of calls for emergency purposes in the local areas. The consequence of this action is that businesses and residences attempting to report life-threatening conditions may well have been blocked at the CO. Conversely, the cellular companies, who offered services in this area, did not attempt TPRS. Their fear was that, in the event they blocked a cellular call from completion in a life-threatening situation, they could be sued for damages.

1.3.4 The quake that never happened

Estimates have been made that a major quake will occur in the east or midwest in the next three to five years. Everyone is aware that the geologists have said that these areas are on larger faults than the San Andreas fault in California. So, these areas must begin preparing for the inevitable earthquake.

How many other quakes have you heard about since that day in October 1989? Others have been recorded, but they were not significant enough to draw major interest.

The exception to this rule was the quake that never took place. In New Madrid, Missouri, the prediction of a major quake on or about December 3 (plus or minus three days), 1990, caused sheer panic in the area. Travel agencies were booking concerned citizens out of the area, the National Guard was placed on alert, schools were canceled for the day, and major utility companies (telephone, electric, and others) cancelled all employee vacations during this period. Although the quake never happened, the loss of productivity, the nightmares for the residents, and the general sense of impending doom all took their toll. However, the biggest concern is, now that the event has passed and the quake did not happen, what the companies, businesses, and residents will do. Most probably, they will go back to life and business as usual, laughing at the big miss. What of the potential risk for the future? Will they merely let their guard down and ignore this risk in the future, only to be devastated if the quake does happen? Do not be lulled into nonaction. Take the first step in planning now!

1.3.5 The Penn Mutual fire

On May 30, 1989, a fire alarm was sounded at the Penn Mutual Insurance Company in Philadelphia, Pennsylvania. Smoke was discovered on the ninth floor of a highrise office building. The area from where the smoke was emanating was the records room. The blaze was horrendous, with the flames causing the temperature to rise in the space up to 2000 degrees. Such intense heat only helped the flames spread even more rapidly. Paper was literally igniting from the heat. Throughout the rest of the day and into the next day, the fire escalated to a nine-alarm condition, with upwards of 450 to 500 firefighters involved.

The fire was located above the data center. Millions of gallons of water were being poured onto the fire, which resulted in the water flowing down to the data center. Ceiling tiles were destroyed and the flow of water was causing extensive damage to their systems.

Penn Mutual had a disaster recovery plan in place, so *disaster* was declared to SunGard Recovery Services (a company specializing in providing hot site facilities). As a result, Penn Mutual was able to relocate their critical files and personnel to the SunGard hot site and get back into service by noon the next day. Coincidentally, they had already begun to move most of their people out of the Philadelphia office to a new site in Horsham, Pennsylvania, a suburb of Philadelphia. Therefore, they had to establish communications to these offices. They used a T1 (a digital line providing 24 channels multiplexed together over a four-wire circuit) and some dial backup facilities to communicate with their offices around the country while in the recovery mode. SunGard had sufficient communications capabilities to handle Penn Mutual's needs. It was obvious that the restoration phase was going to take a significant amount of time, so Penn Mutual needed to migrate from the hot site to a cold site. This process required a three-step approach:

First, move from the original site to the hot site

Second, move from the hot site to a cold site

Third, move from the cold site to the newly constructed site

Each of these moves introduces an element of risk. Damage may happen every time you move equipment.

How do you think your organization would fare in a similar situation? Are you there, or are you totally exposed? That's what this is all about!

1.4   OTHER DISASTERS AFFECTING TELECOMMUNICATIONS

The major disasters were all covered by the press, bringing an awareness to the business community. However, others of significant consequences occurred, but may not have gathered the same amount of coverage. These disasters, which are the more significant ones, are not the only others to have happened. As mentioned before, hundreds of isolated (company, site, branch, etc.) disasters occur all the time, with mere mentions in the press.

1.4.1   AT&T's network

On January, 15, 1990, at approximately 2:30 p.m., a software glitch in AT&T's network caused a severe limitation in the processing of switched services nationwide for AT&T customers. This glitch was propagated by a logic error in the SS7 network. The problem, which had been resident for some time, only became a problem when a series of events culminated in the actual use of these lines of code. Fortunately, this event took place on a holiday, Martin Luther King

Day, which minimized the severity of the disaster, because government offices, banks, etc., were closed for the day. However, for a period of nine hours, the network was reduced to a crawl, slowing down the ability of customers to place calls. Fortunately for the user base, alternatives existed in the design of the network. Many users were able to use the other carriers' services, such as Sprint and MCI Communications. Each of these carriers stated that it had sufficient capability to carry the added traffic. However, what if this had happened on a normal business day? Could these two carriers really support the demands of the customer calls?

A second problem occurred on AT&T's network in June of 1990 just north of Atlanta. On a major fiber optic route, a construction company was digging along the fiber right-of-way, where the cables are buried. In this instance, the contractor dug up the fiber cables and severed them three times in one day. The magnitude of this problem was that over 230 DS3 equivalents (a DS3 is the digital equivalent of 672 circuits multiplexed together) were disrupted.

1.4.2   Illinois Bell

In October 1990, Illinois Bell had a similar cable cut. A contractor, who was planting trees along a cable right-of-way, placed his auger into the ground and proceeded to dig up the equivalent of 80,000 circuits on the fiber and copper cables buried beneath the ground. Unfortunately, one of the COs affected by this outage was Hinsdale, the CO that had burned to the ground two-and-a-half years prior to this event. Had the contractor waited another two months, the Hinsdale office would have been protected from this outage. Illinois Bell was in the process of building a dual ring between the COs to prevent disruptions from cable cuts. Unfortunately, disasters strike when we least expect them.

1.4.3   The Consolidated Edison fire

On August 13, 1990, a fire in a ConEdison substation caused a blackout in the lower Manhattan financial district. This was listed as the worst single regional power-related disaster in the history of the disaster recovery industry. The initial reaction was that since many of the companies affected had backup power capabilities, the problems would be minimal. Unfortunately, in any disaster, nothing goes according to plan. Several companies had backup power systems, but had not tested them for some time. Therefore, they could not get back on line because the generators would not start, either because of fouled fuel or already failed commercial power needed by the pumps. In this area—the financial district, Wall Street, and the World Trade Center—many customers were affected by this outage. What was reassuring was that many of the financial houses were able to relocate to their hot site companies and get back into business quickly. Some 11,000 customers were affected by the loss of power, which, according to ConEdison, lasted approximately eight hours. However, some of the customers were stricken for nearly six days.

How do you think your organization would fare if you lost power for eight hours to six days? Could your company survive the financial consequences? Think, too, that the power-related problem appears to be an inconvenience, since you can give employees natural daylight to work by. However, power is essential for all of our data processing, automation, and communications facilities and equipment.

2

Getting Started?

2.1 THE PRELIMINARY PLAN

2.1.1 Historical facts

In order to get support and financial backing from your management, it is obvious that you will have to convince them of the need for a disaster recovery plan. You will convince them with a valid business plan. This can take on many forms. One is a method of showing senior management what the impact on the business will be without the plan. So, for now, you should consider the consequences. Many of today's managers are acutely aware of the situations that have transpired in industry (no industry is immune) where the business entity (company, firm, supplier, carrier) is in jeopardy of sustaining day-to-day operations when disasters strike.

However, telecommunications managers (or those responsible for the telecommunications function in the organization: administrative managers, office managers, etc.) have a tendency to describe needs in nonbusiness terms. They use telecommunications terms with which they are comfortable (i.e., to provide diverse routing, requirements for redundant statistical multiplexors, etc.). Then, they wonder why management is somewhat unenthusiastic about their requests. The primary reason is obvious to the lay person: management neither understands what is being said, nor cares about the technical terms being used! They are far more comfortable with a business proposition.

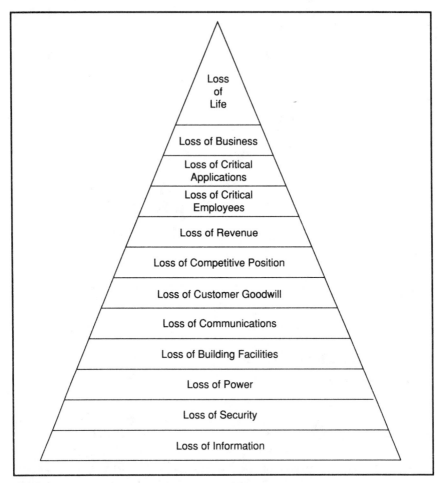

Figure 2.1   What constitutes a disaster? This is a compilation of information by various users. The items are not rank ordered, since they vary by organization.

When you use their terms, a reckoning of the severity of the situation takes place.

For example, you could tell management that, without a plan in place, they would risk a severe decrease in market share in the event of a disaster.

The organization can only survive as an entity if a plan is in place to reestablish communications capabilities within 24 or 48 hours.

Some examples to use when discussing this with management are outlined in Figure 2.1, "What constitutes a disaster?" This figure represents a compilation of user input from around the country, regardless of the size or the industry segment. The ideas are not rank ordered by priority, since they will vary in importance by organization.

2.2   NETWORKING WITH OTHERS

Management of any organization deals with business issues. The above examples will get their attention, but you have to be prepared to answer their questions as well. If challenged, how do you get their support for the survivability issues? Here is where the networking portion of the planning process comes into play. Before you ever get your audience with management, you should work with key departments in the organization. Recruit their assistance in pulling information together for you. Some of the key people you might want to use are listed. Of course, this will depend on your own organization.

Corporate Controller
This is an individual who can put numbers together for you, and those numbers become his or hers, not yours. So, if management challenges your presentation of a number, the controller is supportive and prevents the program from getting bogged down.

V.P. / Director Operations
What more critical aspect would be affected if operations would come to a standstill? The senior operations executive will be very concerned if you convince him or her that the loss of communications would impact production. This executive can now act as a champion with senior management, carrying your message to the board, suggesting that a plan must be enacted to prevent disruptions to operations.

Internal / External Auditors
The internal and external auditors carry a lot of weight within the organization. A message from them in their reports (preparing for the loss of communications is equally as important as data processing and computers) gets a significant degree of attention. Although most of us cringe when the auditors come around, and feel that they are the "enemy," it is time to consider them for what they really represent. They are the corporate watchdogs, with a measure of authority and respect to give management a realistic review of their policies, procedures, and practices. If they see areas that need improvement, it is their charter to highlight them as action items. These action items, when supported by management, become hot buttons on everyone's "to-do list." So, if you can recruit the auditors' assistance in bringing the potential problem to management, you can expect management's support when you are prepared to address the situation.

V.P. / Director Human Resources
Human resources will be concerned with the impact of a disaster as it would pertain to protecting the corporation's most critical asset: human life. Everyone knows that a dollar value cannot be placed on a life. It is our first and foremost responsibility. Human resources

will also be a big help later on in the process when you look for inventories of people. For now, get their support in approaching management with the need for a plan.

Site Managers
Each person who is chartered to run the operation of a single or multiple site(s) will have a vested interest in providing input to your basic presentation to management. Use your resources wisely. You will find not only a supporter of the program, but a potential pool of help when you need it the most. A site coordinator, either the site manager or other designated individual, will be needed. You will get far more commitment from a site manager who is supportive of the program.

V.P. Corporate Communications / Public Relations
How do you think your company would look to the public if a disaster struck and no plan was in place to recover? Well, that is how the public relations people would feel. If they are out there in the industry selling the benefits of using your company's product/service, and a disaster would severely impair the company's ability to produce, they would feel ridiculous. So, they will use it as a selling tool to management.

V.P. Sales or Marketing
Once again, these are business managers who are out there in industry, fighting for every percentage point of market share they can get. What impact would they suffer if all communications were lost for a period of time (hours, days, weeks)? You will find a lot of support for your planning process here! The sales organizations are critically tied to their ability to communicate with customers, distributors, etc. Telecommunications is that essential resource that allows them to do their job.

Now that you have got some supporters, you may have an easier time getting to senior management. Figure 2.2 represents this high-level steering committee who will be useful in getting the assistance. The organizational heading is strictly for the purpose of illustration, rather than reporting structure. However, the key ingredient is to solicit the department heads listed. Getting the commitment from these high-level executives will not be easy. They are typically quite busy, but without their support you may struggle to gain commitment from other departments. So be persistent. Ask each of these high-level supporters, or their designee, to assist in putting together a business case for management. If you use their information, have them put the information in writing, or be able, in an executive-level meeting, to support *their* numbers and information (not yours). When all heads go

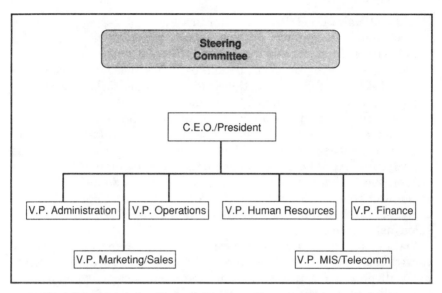

Figure 2.2 Organizing for disaster recovery. The organization for the steering committee should include the highest-level person you can get.

up and down at the same time (in the affirmative), then management typically will not challenge your input. You will be allowed to continue with your presentation.

2.3 DO YOUR HOMEWORK

After conducting the preliminary information gathering, the need to prepare a presentation to management still looms in the future. Prior to getting in front of management, you must take the necessary steps to think through the process. How are you going to suggest the need for a disaster recovery plan without getting thrown out the door? Many managers feel that by bringing attention to the networks and the risks facing the organization, they are equally exposing themselves to the risk of getting fired. Take faith in your management. They are accustomed to dealing with risk and the possibilities of loss. Their forte is the ability to mitigate the risk through a detailed understanding of the business impact based on the conduct of risk assessments of products, services, and new campaigns. Thus, you will be far better off by allowing your management the opportunity to understand and evaluate their exposures rather than trying to hide them.

Suppose you work for an organization with stodgy management. The opportunity still exists to win them over. Many industries are regulated or required by regulation to have a disaster recovery plan in place. "In place" assumes that the plan is a good one, which has been tested and maintained through a coordinated set of testing procedures. To sell your management on this aspect, you may get away with merely citing the applicable regulations affecting your business.

Does this relieve you of all obligations? No, not even if you have apprised your management of the risks to their networks, telecommunications, and data communications, and they reject your assessment. You are still obligated to hammer away at them. Should legal proceedings emanate as the result of a disaster, the courts will not look favorably on a manager who has surfaced an element of risk, then backed away from the heat because management was reluctant. The burden is still on the individual manager to prove beyond a doubt that a need exists and that something must be done. Your legal obligations are based on prudence and due diligence. Be prepared for the long-term sales task ahead of you.

You must understand that before making this important presentation, this is a *command decision and you expect approval.* You should not walk into a meeting with your senior management hoping that they will approve your request. That would be a self-defeating proposition. Moreover, your lack of confidence will show through, posing an opportunity to get smothered with objections.

2.4   WHAT ABOUT THAT ALL-MPORTANT PRESENTATION?

Be upbeat, be positive, be confident, and accept management's questions/interruptions as constructive. *Do* use their questions as opportunities to reinforce your points, rather than letting them frustrate you. A lot of highly qualified, intelligent people, are an absolute flop when trying to deliver a presentation to management. They suffer from fear of public speaking. Although they have put together an outstanding plan, they fall flat on their faces when they try to present it. As a result, they are sent away with no decision or a series of questions/ added items to address. Unfortunately, they probably had the answers with them all the time. Regrettably, they lose too much time and effort when this occurs. How do you get around it?

If you suffer from stage fright and have to present the plan to your senior management, what will you do? You may try to develop the necessary skills before going in front of the board, but this takes time and experience. You can recruit someone else to do it for you. Here is where the assets, such as the key people listed earlier (i.e., the V.P. of public relations or the V.P. of sales), can present either all or part of the plan for you. They are very qualified to do it. A word of caution: make sure you retain ownership of the program. Oftentimes someone who does the presentation starts to feel a stronger commitment and begins to take ownership of it. Use your resources to your advantage.

So just what are you going to tell your management? Some ideas you may consider are:

1. Introduction: Just why are you here in front of them?
2. Historical facts: Who has been affected by disasters and how have they survived? Use same industry examples where possible.
3. What are your exposures? Be frank and explain *your* risks as opposed to industry risks.
4. What will the impact be on your/their business?
5. What can be done to prevent major outages? The operative word is *prevention*, a preferred method over recovery.

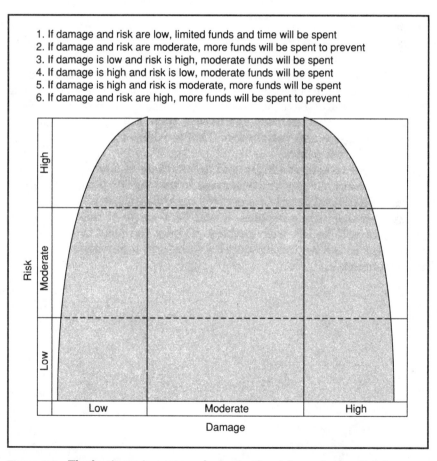

Figure 2.3 The business impact analysis. As the risks and potential damages both move toward the high/high quadrant, more funds will be devoted to the prevention process.

6. What steps will have to be taken to develop a plan? This will include any options you have available.

7. What resources/staff will be needed? This includes both the development of the plan and the ongoing maintenance and testing.

8. An estimate of the cost to produce the plan. The cost has to be all-inclusive for human resources and options (consultants, programs, awareness, etc.).

9. The length of time necessary to put the plan together. This has to be realistic in terms of putting the plan together. Make sure you stay on schedule.

10. The possible legal liabilities that will exist if a plan is not in place. This covers several legal aspects, such as contracts, industry requirements, and shareholders.

These issues can be represented in a pictorial format as depicted in Figure 2.3, "The business impact." The chart represents an analysis of the degree of risk (stated in high, medium, and low) and the degree of loss (stated in high, medium, and low) that can be expected on a two-axis system. As the axis moves to a high degree of risk and a high degree of loss, management can assess their role in supporting the plan for recovery and restoration. This is where the funds will go to shore up the risk points.

Remember to keep it simple, and *talk to them in their terms.*

This is one of the most critical steps in getting the planning process started. Additional details are covered regarding these issues. If you do not get management's support, it will be a waste of time to proceed. Thus, you will be left with nothing. Taking the time to develop the awareness in the beginning stages will help in many more ways than you can imagine.

The Planning Process

3.1 PRESENTING THE PLAN TO MANAGEMENT

Once you have done your homework, considered the historical facts, talked to others, and come to a realization that the presentation to senior management is necessary, you can begin the final stages of preparing for the ever-so-important presentation. To do this, a format for the presentation may follow certain lines.

3.1.1 Gathering the facts

This segment of your presentation to management will be the culmination of the work you have already done. It will be the logical flow of information to create the awareness of a need. Remember again, this is the business assessment of the need for the plan, not a technical assessment.

1. Introduction:
   The opportunity exists to address the key concept of disaster recovery and business resumption planning for networks, telecommunications, and data communications systems. You may want to have an estimate of just what you are spending annually for telecommunications services. Try to put together an estimate of revenues derived from this investment. If you can show a direct relationship

of telecommunications dollars spent to revenues/profits derived, you have a good basis to show management just what it is that they are trying to protect.

2. Historical Facts:
How many companies do you know of that have suffered from disasters? A few are listed in the beginning of this book, but hundreds exist of which you never heard. Do some research in your industry, geographic area, etc. You may be surprised at what you learn. Next, try to put some dollar value to other companies' losses from a historical perspective. If you hear of any companies who folded as a direct result of a disaster because they could not sustain the losses, use that information. It goes a long way toward convincing management that this is serious business. After the Hinsdale fire, several small businesses went out of business due to the loss of communications and the inability to fall back on a disaster recovery plan. So even though the Bell Operating Company had the problem, its impact was far-reaching, down through its customer base.

1989 was the year of disasters. There were over 29 natural disasters alone, including earthquakes, floods, hurricanes, severe cold, tornadoes, lightning, and others. 1990 kept pace with everything that happened in 1989, so you have two good years of comparative information to show management.

Add to the natural causes (acts of God) the human-error-caused types of disasters: fires, floods from broken pipes, power outages, viruses, hackers, cut cables, etc., and you have got a strong story to tell.

3. What are your exposures (risks)?
This is more specific. What areas are you exposed to in your particular environment? Try to be realistic; *do not use scare tactics* here, but a matter-of-fact approach. Identify all of your weak points; in some cases this will get far more detailed when you go beyond the initial presentation and begin your complete inventory (more on that later). If you can provide a global overview to management, they will have an appreciation of your needs, and be more receptive to funding the planning process.

4. What would be the impact on the business?
The key people you recruit will be helpful in getting this message across. You will have to start with a business impact analysis. Once again, this is something that you have to address in business terms. Somewhere along the line the key people will give you their input on each of the areas below, and by using their numbers, assessments, etc. (and not your numbers), you will have more credibility in presenting these to management.

3.1.2   The business impact analysis

Some of the areas you will have to address are as follows (this is typically called a business impact analysis):

1. Determine the potential risks.
2. Determine the probability of the event occurring.
3. Estimate the impact or cost of the occurrence.
4. Identify the remedies you can take to fix or better prevent it.
5. How long would the event impair service or business functionality?
6. What would be the cost to fix the problem?
7. What priorities would exist (what risks do you minimize first, etc.)?
8. How long would it take to put the fix in place?

To better understand the business impact, a graphical presentation may be better than words. Table 3.1 is a representation of another business impact analysis format, which is easier to represent to management.

3.1.3   Example of a loss

Let's use a simple example of how you might show a lost revenue case from the loss caused by a disaster. I will set the stage with the following assumptions:

There is a fire in your PBX room, which totally destroys your PBX and all the backboards (MDF), melts the wires, etc. The fire will put you out of business for three weeks minimum. The company is a 150-employee organization, using a state-of-the-art digital PBX with automated attendant, voice message, and Automatic Call Distributor (ACD) capabilities. The function of the company is telemarketing with 100 agents calling clients and future business prospects (the agents

TABLE 3.1 The Business Impact of a Disaster								
Risk	Risk factor	Impact	Cost of loss	Length of outage	Steps to prevent	Cost	Priority	Time to implement

average $45,000 annual salary, benefits, and incentives), and selling a very competitive high-ticket-cost product. The industry has limited competition, and there is no significant price advantage among companies. Thus, there is no brand loyalty. The customer can use a product from any one of the competitors with equal satisfaction. The main competitive edge is provided through customer service. A market survey was conducted and the following assumptions were made. Your company commands 55 percent of the market share of a $2 billion industry. Customers will call your company and if the phone is not answered in three rings they will hang up and go to the next supplier. In the event of a disaster, market surveys state that 60 percent of your customers would be willing to wait one day for you to solve your problems before going to a competitor; only 30 percent would wait up to one week for you to solve the problem; none will wait any longer. This means that after one week, all of your customers will go elsewhere for the product. If your company survives the disaster, it will have to introduce a whole new marketing effort to recapture the lost customer base at great cost. Let's play out some numbers. See Table 3.2 for the business case of a loss.

What is the probability of this scenario happening to you? Can your organization sustain these losses?

These are hard questions that you personally probably will not be able to answer, but your advertising, operations, financial, and insurance departments will help put the information together.

TABLE 3.2 Case Example of a Loss After a Disaster			
Industry size	$2 billion		
Anticipated losses from a fire		$63,346,152	
Productivity lost ($865 per emp x 100 x 3 weeks)		$259,000	
Cost to rebuild the systems			
New PBX		$150,000	
Wiring at $200 per line		$30,000	
ACD system		$40,000	
Voice mail/auto attendant		$60,000	
UPS/battery backup		$35,000	
Installation		$20,000	
Fire detection/suppression		$10,000	
Room construction		$25,000	
Marketing campaign to regain share		$2,000,000	
Total cost of the loss			$65,975,672

Let's suppose you could have installed a fire detection/suppression system before this happened, and you were better positioned to deal with the situation with the implementation of your new disaster recovery plan. The cost could have been minimized to a net opportunity expense of the plan and the fire system. For comparative purposes the installation of the plan and fire systems may have cost you (sample numbers) $70,000 to $100,000.

Do you think your management would be somewhat supportive of your efforts now?

3.1.4 Additional items

Other items will have to be covered when addressing your management. Some of these will include the following:

1. Contracts that can be set up to help in the prevention mode, or whatever can be done in advance to accommodate the ability to recover quickly from the loss of equipment, networks, and/or facilities. Oftentimes this simple step of having a contractual arrangement in place (in advance) can make the difference between a minor and a major disaster.

2. Policy and procedures changes are necessary to implement the plan. Some of the existing personnel and administrative policies may have to change due to the actions/reactions after a disaster. This should be carefully reviewed for all changes and contradictions as they occur. If you work in a union shop environment, the Human Resources Department may have to prearrange for special provision in the Labor Contract. Does your company's contract preclude working your people extra hours, abnormal shifts, and relocating to a hot site out of town? Check this out before you need to do it.

3. Look at legal liabilities from both the organizational level and a contractual level. We have already seen that certain industries are required by law to have a disaster recovery plan in place, but other risks exist that may not be as obvious, such as:

   - The role of the senior management in the corporation is to maximize shareholder wealth, protect the organization from legal suits, and nurture the growth and profitability of the organization. If, as a result of a disaster, the organization suffers damages and/or losses which could have been either prevented or minimized with a plan, the shareholders may well have a claim against management within the organization for not providing due diligence in protecting their investments.

   - Another scenario, which can be of equal import, is the contractual liability for the delivery of goods or services within a contracted period of time. For example, with the "just in time" manufacturing cycles being enjoyed at many major manufacturing organizations, the client/customer will place an order for "X" amount of product to be delivered within a specified time frame. If the product is not delivered in this time frame, the customer may stand to lose business or, worse, customers of its own. Now, your organization is in a position to jeopardize the livelihood of the customer if you do not deliver on time. Thus, the customer has to use a penalty or default clause in its contract with your company for nonperformance. This can be in the form of lost business, consequential damages, or some other arrangement. The loss of telecommunications, data communications, or your network could impair the ability to satisfy the requirements of the contract with the customer. Thus, the senior managers should be aware that they are exposed to a double-edged consideration.

4. Check insurance requirements and costs. The opportunity exists to reduce the cost of insurance if a disaster prevention and recovery plan is in place. Many of the major insurance carriers base their rates for insurance on the amount of claims that may have to be paid out against a certain risk. Risk analyses are conducted based on historical facts and past events requiring a claim to be filed. With a coordinated plan and the training in place to both prevent and recover from a disaster, the insurer has less risk. This means it may offer reductions in the insurance rates necessary for your organization. Check with your insurance carrier, or internal insurance department, to see what assistance can be offered.

5. Regulations may be in existence requiring a plan (based on your industry).

Although these may seem beyond the scope of the telecommunications planning process, you may be surprised (unpleasantly) if you do not consider them in advance. All too often, communicators forget the basic rule of remembering what business they are in, and what the corporate charter is. The mission statement for your department should be in support of the total organization, and not limited to the communications and/or the computer functions. You will be better served when you realize this subtle change of thinking.

Do not forget some dialogue on the methodology necessary to develop the plan. Management needs to understand that there will be some associated costs with putting the plan together. Options exist. The differences in options are varied, and the related costs for each will be significant. You may be looking at developing a plan because of management's query about what is being done in this area. As a result, assume that there is some awareness of the need for telecommunications disaster planning. It may have come from an audit report, a newspaper article, a trade magazine report, or just a discussion with some other executive. At any rate you will have to decide the best proactive approach to use, depending on the time, resources, and money you have/need.

3.2   OPTIONS IN DEVELOPING YOUR PLAN

What are some of your options in developing your plan?

First

You can attempt to develop the plan in-house with existing people and equipment. Time and equipment costs are associated with that. There is also a risk that the time to develop the plan just will not exist because of daily responsibilities and firefighting we all go through. Thus, this project starts to get pushed into the background of our minds. This can be flirting with danger, since you have stated you will get the plan developed with in-house staff. The cost to do this can range from approximately $100,000 to over $200,000, depending on the resources and equipment you commit.

Second

Since the auditors may have brought this to management's attention, you could suggest that the company use them to help develop the plan. The big eight accounting firms are all becoming very proactive in assisting companies to develop these plans. They are not inexpensive, but they do have management's ear and respect in most cases. Further, they can get as many people as needed to get the job done quickly.

Third

Hundreds of independent consultants operate in the industry today who can be hired to work with you on the plan. Their expertise and costs are subject to individual review. A caution here: do not let any consultant or other party write your plan for you. You have to be an active participant in the research and development of the plan. This plan will become a "living and breathing document," which must be constantly tested and updated. It will not serve you or your organization to have some outsider write it for you. The costs for consultants can vary, but you can expect to spend from $1000 to $1500 per day, plus expenses, for a good one. Typical costs for an engagement can run upwards of $100,000 to $125,000. You have to decide how to best use your company's money.

Fourth

Recovery service vendors can offer consulting, assistance in plan development, and even a hot/warm/cold site as part of the plan. There are obvious biases built into these organizations' planning processes. They are in the business of selling an insurance policy in the form of a contingency site. Therefore, it is only fair that you should expect them to recommend their own services. Costs for this assistance would be tied into their services performed and contingency site services subscribed to.

Fifth

A series of PC-based packages are available on the market which can be used to help you develop your plan. This is a common tool used by the finance and banking industries and the military. Once again, many options exist from the very basic to the very elaborate. Some of these packages are beefed-up versions of project management software packages. Still, others are combinations of powerful databases, word processors, project management, and spreadsheet packages. Each in turn runs the gambit of pricing based on the modules you select and the complexity you require. The best way of approaching these packages is to consider the amount of information you need to research and the frequency of changes. Also, ease of use will be an important if not crucial factor. One such package, the Total Business Recovery System (TBRS) by Information Management Technology in Bothell, Washington, is designed around a PC system, which has extensive capabilities. This package covers the gambit of your needs, such as:

1. A Relational Database using Oracle as its layer, giving you the benefits of System Query Language (SQL) and Query by Example (QBE).

2. The common powerful word processing packages, such as Microsoft Word and WordPerfect.

3. The common spreadsheet packages, such as Lotus 123 and Microsoft Excel.

4. A graphics-based package for creating graphs, charts, and flow charts, such as Harvard Graphics.

5. A time line management package for the tracking of the project, such as Total Project Manager and TimeLine.

Many of the others have similar capabilities based on either standard packages off the shelf, or custom designed systems. These packages can range from inexpensive to expensive, depending on the modules and pricing schemes used.

Recruiting the Team

4.1 RECRUITING THE TEAM

There are several issues you will have to deal with when the recruitment step comes along:

- Just who should you involve on the team?
- How many people should be involved?
- What departments should they be from?
- Who maintains control of them?
- How do you assign them tasks?

There are no easy answers here. It all depends on the individual organization. However, one thing is for certain: you can make mistakes! You have to be somewhat selective in recruiting your team members, both from internal and external sources. The wrong people on the team can bog down the process. What is needed most is a small group of contributors who are individually committed to the perpetuity of the business.

Some suggestions on how others have done this are enclosed on the following pages. This again is not the be-all and end-all, but a summary of some ideas that have worked.

4.2   JUST WHO SHOULD YOU INVOLVE ON THE TEAM?

The issue of who to recruit also deals with how you should recruit team members. There are various departments in the organization who have vested interests in the availability of telecommunications facilities and networks for the successful completion of their mission. Some of these departments will include (to name a few):

- Marketing/Telemarketing
- Sales
- Production
- Purchasing
- Data Processing/MIS
- Finance/Accounting
- Telecommunications
- Operations/Operations Management

Organizing your working teams will possibly include a select cadre of members. Figure 4.1 lists the possible organizational functions that are candidates to offer assistance in the development and implementation of the plan. You have to select the group as functions pertain to your organization. The organizational chart is informal in reporting structure, but formal in responsibilities.

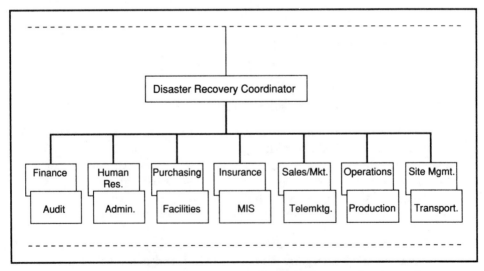

Figure 4.1 Working committee plan development. The organization and structure for the working committee depends on the individual organization.

Each of these organizations has a vested interest in the use of telecommunications to get their jobs done. Therefore, they are likely candidates to select from within the organization. You can gain their acceptance and support in a number of ways.

The first might be to build an awareness in their minds of how critical the telecommunications function is to them. This can be done in the form of a questionnaire to the department heads, senior managers in each area, and, if dealing with remote sites, the individual site managers.

Structure and content of the questionnaire are important. You want to keep the questions as nontechnical as possible. The best results will come from open-ended questions that deal with the department's use of the technologies and services you provide and manage for them. They will usually follow through and give you some critical information. This will start to generate some thought processes in their own minds concerning their needs, and should translate into some key areas that need to be addressed.

Functionally, since this is a telecommunications issue, the MIS department may be responsible for the telecommunications area (voice/data/video/networks). Figure 4.2 is a representation of the MIS function with the telecommunications responsibility. This is the best of both worlds since a single plan can address all of the aspects of the telecomm function, and a plan may already be in place addressing the other areas, making it easier to integrate the plans.

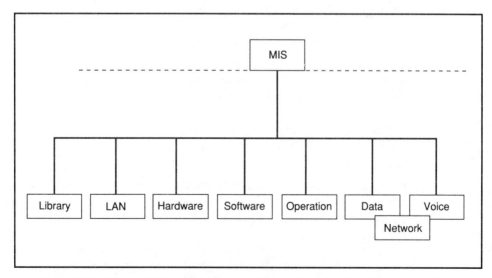

Figure 4.2   MIS and telecomm recovery team. Covering the full range of networks and services, this may be the best of both worlds.

4.3   BUILD AN AWARENESS

The awareness program, as mentioned, can begin with a questionnaire that you ask the department/division/site managers to fill out. Structure it so that they have the opportunity to answer in their own words. Some typical questions might be:

- Please describe how your department functions.
- Just how important is the telephone to your everyday operation?
- How many calls do you make/receive per day? Your department? Your division?
- Of the calls made and received per day, what percentage are internal? What percentage are external?
- What about other forms of communications? Do you have a PC/terminal/other device hooked up to a modem?
- Do you have a Facsimile (FAX) within your organization? If so, how many send/receive copies per day?
- What would be the impact to your organization if we lost all communications capabilities for a period of an hour? a day? a week? a month?
- If the above situation occurred, could you fall back to some other manual system, such as mail, runner, or courier service, and still service your accounts/departments/users?
- What do you think it would cost (in dollars/good will/competitive edge) the company if such an event occurred? How much of your revenue is derived from the use of the telephone, FAX, data communications?
- Do you periodically review the operation of your department to test what might happen if a total failure of telecommunications would occur?
- Do you have certain critical applications that must be available at all times? How would you prioritize them in comparison to other departments' needs?
- If we had a partial failure of our networks and facilities, and had to operate for some period of time in a degraded service mode, what applications would you want supported first?

There is nothing magical about this type of questionnaire, other than it may cause the individual managers to take a new look at their dependency on a service that so many take for granted. Oftentimes, you may already know the answers to these questions before you send them out. Be that as it may, it provokes thought and starts to generate interest, so use it or some other form of awareness.

Another form of awareness may come from an information program. There are ways such as:

1. Start copying and sending copies of articles dealing with disasters to your senior managers, department/division managers, etc.

2. If you have an internal newspaper or publication, put thought-provoking ideas in there, such as: "What would you do if the lights went out?". . . or "Did you ever wonder how quiet the office would be if all the phones stopped ringing at once?" . . . or "How well could you support your customers if you could not talk to them for awhile and had to use the mail?". . . or "What would you do if you came to work tomorrow, and the guards would not let you in because the building was flooded from a burst pipe or burned out due to a fire?"

Use your imagination and you can come up with far more ideas than we can expound upon here, but by all means do something to create the awareness in your organization. Then the recruitment will get easier for you. The big thing is to get started as quickly as possible. The clock is running and the cards are stacked against you!

4.4   STAFFING ISSUES

4.4.1   Where do you get the people?

Once you have started the awareness program, the next issue in the process will be the staffing you will have to deal with. How many people do you need on your team? If the answer was as simple as stating a finite number, we could probably end right here, but it is never that simple.

The best thoughts you can use would be to recruit a manageable number of people who are dedicated enough to commit the necessary time and energy to the program, and who are responsible enough to get whatever assistance they need from their individual groups. Simply stated, use only as many as you feel are absolutely necessary. If you gain the acceptance from the department or divisional management of your organization, this should all fall into place. A word of caution, however. Do not let them just pick a name from a list or a hat. Try to recruit their assistance directly, but if they feel they must assign the task to one of their subordinates, get approval to interview the candidate before acceptance. This gives you the opportunity to the right of first refusal.

Why is that so important? There were several people who embarked on a mission of developing a plan, and when interviewing the senior department/division manager, were told that they could use "Person X" from that group. Unfortunately, this person did not really see the need for the program, and was more committed to getting his or her normal job done. So, when tasks were assigned, "X" had a tendency to let the tasks slide, and oftentimes never gave any indication that he or she had not put any effort into the project. When the project coordinator asked for input, being put on the spot, this person either came up with a series of excuses why the work was not completed, or worse, fabricated answers which were totally irrelevant. So be careful.

4.4.2   How do you get them?

A simple way of getting the support might be to meet with the department/divisional manager as a follow-up to the responses on the questionnaire. At that time, this interview will be a clarification of points brought up by the manager. Here is the opportunity to ask that manager for his or her help by being on the team to collect necessary information to put into the plan. The manager may well volunteer, but also may state that he or she is too busy, and would like to assign "John" to the task at hand. I found that if you come back with a requirement to interview John on the spot with the manager present, you keep the door open to suggest another person. John will feel the pressure of being volunteered, but you will probably pick up on his resistance in the interview. If you do, suggest that the manager give you some alternative team members, so you can pick the one you feel more comfortable with. This usually works quite well. Remember, you have to maintain control over the team and the entire situation.

If John should work out, then you can expect a dedication from him to get the tasks accomplished in a timely manner. Here again, you may need the assistance of the manager. Suppose John has more to do than one person can be expected to accomplish in a timely manner. The manager may volunteer to let John recruit any assistance he needs to get the job done. He will have the responsibility and the authority to act on behalf of the manager. Now you will have a winning combination!

4.4.3   What departments should the team be from?

This is the next issue you will have to deal with. If you start the recruitment effort correctly, and all of the departments are sincerely interested in the program, you should be selective. Try to get the key people and departments covered, but do not go for overkill. There are a certain number of key areas that absolutely should be represented on your team. Others are optional. These are departments that you have to figure out based on your individual situation, but again try to limit the amount of team members to a manageable number.

Some of the other key areas that should be on the team might include (all of this depends on your specific company and how it is organized):

Vendors

Carriers

Insurers

Firefighters

Police officers

Building managers

4.5   BUILDING THE HYPE!

This is one of the areas that starts the process of collecting information off to a jump start. If you handle it properly, you will get the commitment from the team members to carry through the project with a dedication that will be unsurpassed. People in general are looking for recognition for a job well done. That is easily enough handled if they do what is expected of them, but what about those that do not meet your expectations? Sometimes, peer pressure can be a far better motivator than punishment, reward, rebuke, etc. So, you have to build the hype in these team members to a point that they are truly devoted to accomplishing the project.

There are some inexpensive ways of handling this. Some ideas that may (or may not) work for you are:

- Try a kickoff meeting with the team. Get as much "press coverage" as possible on who they are and what they are doing. The internal newsletter in your organization is a useful tool for this.

- Have regular meetings. Perhaps a breakfast meeting, weekly, where the information flow can begin. The company cafeteria can be a useful location for this weekly meeting. You want to keep these meetings as short and to the point as possible. Once the meeting is finished, the team members are close to their respective workplace, and are not being kept away from their normal responsibilities unreasonably long.

- Have some form of recognition for them. Perhaps it will be a sticker that can be placed on their desk, name plate, or other noticeable location. This will be an attention getter in their departments. It will also serve as a locator for other company personnel to provide input that may be valuable in the data collection stages.

- At each of the meetings, reward those who have completed their assigned tasks since the last meeting. This again can be an inexpensive gift/recognition factor. It can be in the form of a certificate, a "gimme," such as a trinket (i.e., little wind-up "Woodstock dolls"), or a T-shirt with the words, "Disaster Recovery Team Member" on it. You can even talk to management to see if you could sponsor a T-shirt day for your team members (providing it would not conflict with the corporate image and the conduct of business). This again makes these people stand out as special.

- Perhaps you could use a helium balloon with the words "Recovery Team Member" on it tied to the backs of their chairs. This would cause them to be easily recognizable to other members of the company or department as a person who will be responsible for the disaster recovery planning team and as someone who cares about the survivability of the organization. A little bit goes a long way.

- Highlight the team members individually in the internal newsletter. A spotlight on the individual members will boost the awareness of the organization's commitment to the program, and will give each of the team member's egos a little boost too.

- Remember to keep it simple and inexpensive. You are dealing with company funds, and you do not want to be frivolous with large amounts of money that can be spent on disaster planning.

- When the team completes the total job, you could consider a dinner or luncheon. Again, press coverage would be a plus. Here you can recognize the key contributors to the company's business continuity plan. A plaque can be awarded at the final dinner with the senior management involved in making the awards. This is exposure for the individual in the corporate hierarchy as well as something special for a job well done.

A lot of people come to the forefront as super workers when they feel a sense of belonging and pride in what they are doing. You must not lose sight of the importance of the plan, but you should remember the individual efforts that are necessary to accomplish the work. If you truly want people to stay active and interested in the plan, keep the hype going.

Something else happens during all this hype. Management is neither naive nor blind. A certain air will start buzzing in the organization, causing management to notice the efforts being taken. This gains a lot of visibility for the plan, since the hype is causing everyone to be aware. Management can feel a little more comfortable with the process, since there will be constant reminders that work is progressing. Above and beyond that point, you may find more interest at the higher levels in just what is going on. You can get more audiences with higher levels of management, allowing you to recruit their support and give you their ideas and concerns. *This makes for a win-win situation.*

There is nothing written that the development of a plan, with the significance of business survivability, cannot be fun and exciting. It is all up to how you handle it in your particular environment.

4.6 ASSIGNING THE TASKS AND FOLLOWING UP

There is no simple way of stating that this is an important responsibility which you are undertaking. You need the commitment from the team members as well as your own internalized hype. You are with the organization to provide and manage a service and function that is critical to its ongoing livelihood. As a result, additional factors exist that you must be concerned with. You have to develop a series of tasks necessary to put the plan together. These tasks will include the gathering of information from all departments regarding their needs. How long could they survive without these services, and how long could they operate with some form of minimized or degraded service? These factors affect the organization's ability to survive and compete in the marketplace after a disaster and cannot be overlooked. It is incumbent on you to know and understand each of the department's needs and the business environment your company operates in.

Once the requirements are defined, the delegation of tasks is a must. You cannot do it alone. The team has to be supportive, and now that they are hyped, you have to give them their assignments.

- Make sure the task is stated (in writing if possible) with a clearly defined yet simple-to-understand goal.

- Try to give them assignments that can be accomplished in a reasonable amount of time (a week to a month depending on the complexity).

- Make sure you can measure the results in either quantitative or qualitative terms (quantitative is the preferred, since it is measurable).

- Make the task realistic. Do not go overboard with the task, such that no one could accomplish it.

- Follow up on a weekly basis at your progress meetings. If, however, an individual is having problems, be prepared to get added support. Oftentimes team members are reluctant to admit that they need help. This can ultimately catch up to them and slow down the progress of the entire plan.

- Keep a project plan with assignments ongoing. Use a milestone or pert or Gantt chart, so that you can see the bottlenecks in the project as they occur. You will be able to see the entire project at a glance, and know if you are on schedule or not. If one member is bogged down, and others are ahead of schedule, you may be able to divert resources to assist in the area that is behind. This is where team spirit comes in. Building the hype and recognition also builds team spirit.

- Try to stay on schedule at all costs. This is an important project. Give it the level of attention it deserves.

- If you are behind schedule, make it known to all. There may be someone on the team who can help with some added time, but you will have to ask.

- Keep management apprised as much as possible. No one likes surprises. If you keep the dialogue going, you will find management will get the resources or help out themselves.

- Try to have monthly follow-up meetings with management, if possible. This provides the forum for them to give their input, and to make sure your goals are consistent with the business goals and plans. It also reinforces your position. The management team or steering committee can remove roadblocks to the process with a single strategically placed call. Let them participate in the process.

4.7   LOGISTICS

What are the logistical problems that you may encounter?

A myriad of situations will come into play when you begin the process of gathering information. The logistical situation in the context of this chapter deals with the managing and controlling of the information flow. The team members will need some form of a check sheet, a standard report format, and the ability to potentially make graphs and charts. Oftentimes the organization has these capabilities in-house and the problem is moot. However, in the case where these capabilities do not exist, you will have to make provisions to have these tools onsite and readily available for the team members' use. If you already have a series of PCs or a mid-range/mainframe system with terminals, you need only make them available to the team. If, however, you do not have these capabilities, you will have to include them in the budgetary estimate in preparing the plan. Do not make this more complex than it is. Merely be aware of the need for a consistent set of tools for all to use.

Some of the above-mentioned forms you may need are:

- Interview forms for the team members to conduct meetings within their departments, divisions, sites, etc., which ask a series of uniform questions, yet allow for the flexibility to be modified as needed on an individual-case basis.

- Critical application, process, and service identifiers, so that you will have a clear understanding of what needs to be protected and in what priority. This may be in the form of a rating or a weighting system.
- Format for input. Will you use a word processor or will you expect handwritten forms back? What about drawings? How do you assess a value of the application, process, and service? Will you use a spreadsheet, or some other application?
- How will you replenish, change, and modify the forms as the teams get feedback? Will you have the ability to react to changes quickly?
- Should questionnaires be generic with space for unique comments, or will you attempt to force feed the system?
- Will the same format work for a department, a site, and a division? What about the peculiarities of an international site?

All food for thought the planning process must take into consideration. Yet flexibility and constructive criticism are key elements which must be included. Now it is time for the teams to get started.

5

The Inventory Process

5.1 CONDUCTING THE INVENTORY

Now that you have the planning team in place and armed with the necessary tools to gather their information, the inventory process kicks in. First, they will have to establish an inventory of the hardware and software specific devices they have in their own departments. This is not to say you are strictly concerned with counting widgets. You are looking for a comprehensive list of the company's needs, by department, application, and service. It is far more global than strictly an inventory of hardware.

5.1.1 Who should be involved in the inventory process?

Each of the team members should have some input as to what should be inventoried. For example, if you have a telemarketing application, similar to the one used in our cost comparison study:

- Telemarketing will have a definite involvement since it impacts their department the most.

- Purchasing will have to input what equipment they need to have/ emergency agreements to buy equipment in the event of a major loss of the facility.

- Personnel or Human Resources will include an inventory of the people needed to perform this function. This may include skill sets, as well as an inventory of the physical, emotional, and medical problems associated with the employee population. If a particular team member has a physical limitation or medical problem, you should be aware of this up front.

- Finance will have some input as to the amount of dollars or procedures that will have to change in order to collect receivables. Also, finance could set aside petty cash for your team members. Specifically, the cash will be used for incidentals during the recovery process. The suggested amount is $100.00 per member of the recovery team, until other arrangements can be made.

- MIS will have some input on the needs for processing power, in order to sustain the operation for some period of time.

- Telecommunications will need to provide the lines, trunks, and hardware to allow for the transfer of the calls to some remote location.

- Administration may have to provide desks, chairs, supplies, etc. at the alternate site.

Thus, you can see this will be a complete inventory and an assessment of the critical nature of the department's needs all rolled up into one. This is a complex task that can be lengthy and confusing, since the department manager may not know, or may overstate, the criticality of his or her department's contribution to the organization.

5.2   WHAT SHOULD BE INVENTORIED?

5.2.1   Assessing the existing equipment

In essence, everything must be inventoried. However, you will have to deal more with the basic equipment for telecommunications, data communications, networks, and facilities. This is not an attempt to minimize the need to discuss the needs of other departments, but keeping in mind the importance of telecommunications, data communications, and networks in the everyday operations of the organization, these critical systems must be addressed specially.

Let's assume that you can come up with a realistic equipment inventory relatively fast. There will be several pieces you have to look at, starting with:

1. *Internal telecommunications equipment and facilities.* Knowing just what equipment you have on site is the first step. Conducting a physical inventory of all components constituting your equipment and networks is vital to understanding the need for a solid disaster recovery plan. The essential components will include:

- Your telephone system (PBX, Key System, hybrid)

- Peripherals (automatic attendant, voice messaging, SMDR systems)

- Modems and muxes (voice/data/statmuxes, etc.)

- Network hardware (ETN, ESN, T1/T3/DSO, etc.)

2. *Media.* The types of communications media employed in your network are of equal concern. Each one bears its own risks and rewards. To effectively prepare for the inevitable disaster, a mix of services utilizing various media can contribute to an effective and quick recovery. Many of the services are contained in the following types of media.

- Dial-up lines

- Leased lines

- Radios

- Cellular

- Infrared

- VSAT

- Microwave

3. *Data Communications.* Although the distinction between voice telecommunications facilities and networks is almost indistinct, many companies still utilize separate networks and departments to manage these functions. Thus, it would be prudent to compare them both jointly and separately. Once the information enters the network (those of the LECs and IXCs), however, it all becomes digitized into bits of information, which we call "data."

- Modems

- Multiplexors

- Data switches

- Statistical multiplexors

- Controllers

- Front end communications processors

4. *Wiring systems.* The wiring in the internal structure will be dependent on the individual site. However, various methods of wiring the office environment have led to both benefits and risks from a failure and recovery process.

- Wiring systems (voice, data, image)

- Wiring schemes and topologies (LANs, WANs, MANs, etc.)

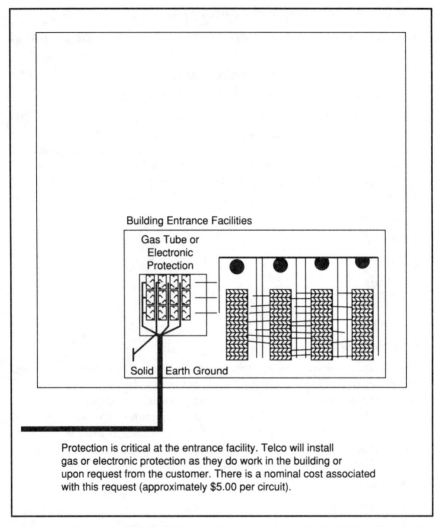

Building Entrance Facilities

Gas Tube or
Electronic
Protection

Solid Earth Ground

Protection is critical at the entrance facility. Telco will install
gas or electronic protection as they do work in the building or
upon request from the customer. There is a nominal cost associated
with this request (approximately $5.00 per circuit).

Figure 5.1 Protect cable facilities at the entrance to the building. Protecting cables at entrance and exit points is necessary.

- Types of wiring (coax, twisted pair, fiber optics)
- Protection on entrance facilities

Figure 5.1 reflects that all entrance and exit cables should be protected from voltage surges, lightning, etc. Telco provides either a carbon block or gas tube protector. Newer systems use an electronic protector which improves the level of protection. This is not automatically installed by the Telco, but can be requested whenever they are working on a cable system.

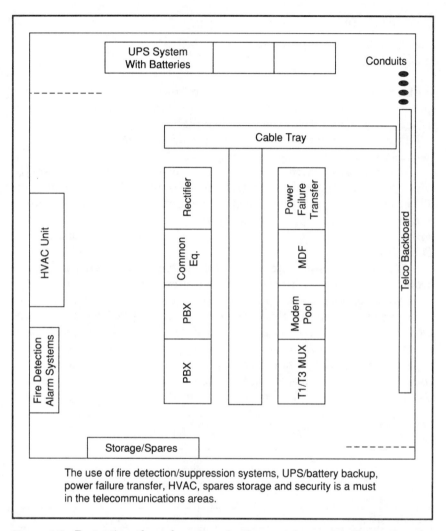

The use of fire detection/suppression systems, UPS/battery backup, power failure transfer, HVAC, spares storage and security is a must in the telecommunications areas.

Figure 5.2 Protecting the telecommunications environment. Protecting the equipment you have in your telecommunications environment is a must.

5. *Physical facility.* The physical facility and the control procedures have a significant impact on the ability to sustain the business operations after a disaster. Once again, each of these components and their design has a bearing on the communications capabilities of the organization.

   - Electrical
   - Security
   - Air conditioning

- Backboards
- Fire detection/suppression
- Entrance points

Figure 5.2 is a representation of the protection systems and components used in a telecommunications environment. These systems are usually overlooked when the room is built.

There are probably other pieces in your specific inventory. Those listed above are the most common. The list should be as inclusive as you can make it, so that you and your organization know exactly what you have. In order to protect the systems and services that you either offer or support, you need to understand just what you have, and what critical support systems are. The use of inventory forms will help you keep the list in a normal sequence, such as outlined on Table 5.1.

It is through this inventory that you can begin to assign priorities to protecting equipment, find voids in maintenance coverage, and work with your vendors to set up maintenance and recovery procedures on the equipment. You can also begin some assessment of the costs to protect the equipment for budgetary purposes. In times of cutbacks and outsourcing, keeping a disaster recovery plan and the associated expenses in the budget becomes extremely difficult. It is incumbent on the reader to have these costs and risks highlighted, so that management will not delete the line items from the budget. Many a senior

TABLE 5.1 Inventory of Equipment		
Item		
Equipment type		
Serial number		
Manufacturer		
Date of purchase		
Used by:		
Used for:		
Critical rating:		
Cost of maintenance		
Maintained by:		
Contract:		
Date of expiration		
Cost to replace		
Other:		

manager feels that disaster recovery is an expense to protect against something that will not happen.

5.2.2 Mapping out the internal facilities

The inventory is only the start. Next, you will begin to map out the facilities. Facilities here will mean the cables brought to your entrance or cable vault in the basement of the building, etc. These are the facilities from the LEC, whether a Bell Operating Company (BOC) or an Independent Operating Company (IOC). However, once the LEC delivers the cable facilities to your demarcation point, it becomes the customer's responsibility to route the cable facilities to the point of need. Further, all maintenance and changes inside the building are customer responsibilities. For the purposes of defining where the customer takes over and the Exchange Carrier stops is a point where the cable is terminated at the point of least penetration in the building. This opens new risks for users in highrise, multitenant buildings. The LEC was allowed, in the past, to bring the service to the customer's demarcation. In the highrise and shared tenant spaces, this meant that the Exchange Carrier brought it to your floor or the equipment room in your space. Whether you were located on the first floor or the twentieth, they got it to you. However, new procedures being outlined by the regulatory bodies state that the Exchange Carrier will terminate the service within 12 inches of the cable head, which is usually in the basement of the building. Running the "house pair and the riser" cables will become the responsibility of the customer. This poses new threats to the recovery process, as well as to any new installations.

Mapping the cabling in an existing building may be difficult at best. Since these cables were part of the Exchange Carrier's inventory, and were used for multiple services and tenants, there are multiple taps and bridges on the wires to accommodate the move and change activity over the years. Now that it will become a customer problem, rewiring or cleanup of the wiring may be required. An extension of this problem is the lack of good recordkeeping over the years. Once again, to determine what is there and where it runs will have an impact on your ability to recover from a disruption of service.

Figure 5.3 is a sample map showing the risers in a highrise building through a diverse cable riser system. This will prevent a single point of failure should something happen inside one of the riser closets.

5.2.3 Mapping the external facilities

You can contact the LEC and request a cable route map from the CO to your entrance. Look for single points of failure along this route. Figure 5.4 depicts a mapping of the local cable routes outside the

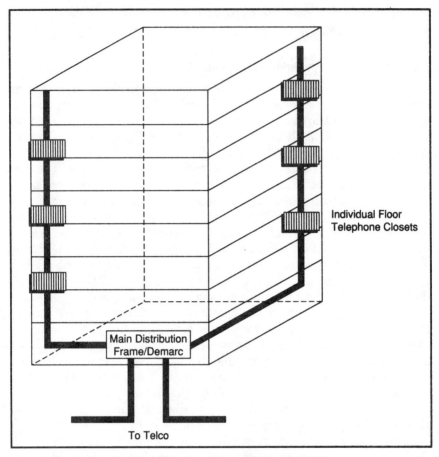

Figure 5.3 Riser, closet, and cable vault diversity. Map out the riser cables within the building, specifically looking for diversity in the cables.

building, again looking for the single point of failure. This should include:

- The route taken
- The circuit designation, number
- The cable pairs assigned by cable, bundle, sheath
- The splice points and handhole locations
- The conduits used
- The vault location
- The entrance point
- The route it takes once inside your building

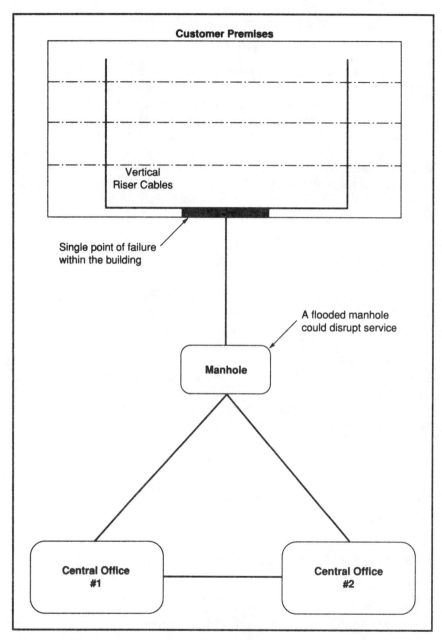

Figure 5.4   Look for single points of failure within your organization. Mapping out the routes from the Central Offices shows the single points of failure along the way.

- The jack, block and pin assignments at the MDF
- Any other information you can get

The map should be both in table form and (if possible) in schematic form. This gives you a graphic representation of your local facilities, so you can see just how your circuits are run. You may be surprised at the information you receive! The exposure points along the route should become fairly obvious. At one point this information was not readily available. However, the LECs are far more cooperative about giving this information to you now that the emphasis on disaster recovery has shifted to a customer concern. You can expect this information to take some time for the LEC to prepare, so build the time into your planning process.

5.2.4 Mapping out the carrier-to-carrier handoff

There is yet another part of this scenario: the connection from the LEC to the IXC facilities. You should ask for the same information from the CO to the IXC's Point of Presence or Point of Termination (POP or POT), depending on what they call it in your area.

You will need to know just what route and equipment you go through from these two points. This will involve some cooperative efforts between the LEC and the IXC or IXCs that you use. Since many companies now use multiple carriers, the need is the same for the information from every POP your service goes through. The information will be similar:

- Circuit designations, numbers
- Routes taken
- Equipment on the route (carrier, DACS, facility)
- Channel numbers
- Conduits
- Cable pairs, or fiber, or channel assignments on a radio system
- Vaults
- Entrance points
- Any other information they are willing to give

Again, you can expect this information to take some time to pull together, but it can be obtained. The efforts of the LECs and the IXCs have increased significantly in their desire to accommodate the customer's requests. A note here: The IXC may have some difficulty giving you the degree of detail outlined here. As you might imagine, this information in the wrong hands will not only expose your network, but also theirs. Thus, many times this information may take on a form of generality to protect all parties.

Figure 5.5 represents a drawing from the carriers showing their network. Once you have this information you can consider protecting your network via a feed from two different COs. This prevents the risk of a single cable cut destroying your entire network.

5.3   WORKING WITH YOUR CARRIERS

Before the process is complete (you need a schematic tied to your inventory), you can begin to work with the vendors. Oftentimes the question arises, "Who do I talk to about all of this information?" So,

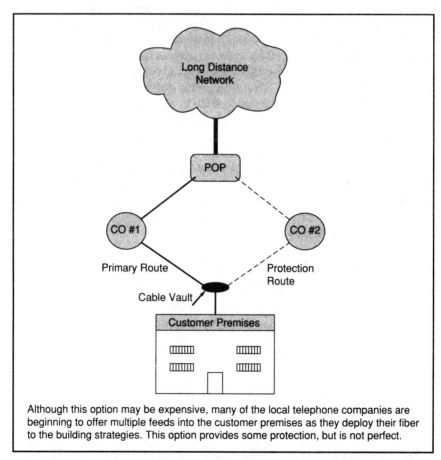

Although this option may be expensive, many of the local telephone companies are beginning to offer multiple feeds into the customer premises as they deploy their fiber to the building strategies. This option provides some protection, but is not perfect.

Figure 5.5   Feeds to two COs provide protection in the event of backhoe fade. Checking the carrier maps will help in determining if feeds from two COs will help prevent a major disruption.

let's take a small step backward, for just a moment. The LECs, IXCs, and the OCCs are all equally concerned about providing the necessary service to all customers. They are also concerned about the damage that could ensue in the event of a disaster. Thus, since the Hinsdale fire, most of these carriers have established teams to assist customers with their requests for information. Although it may vary slightly, the teams are usually contacted through the normal account team assigned to your particular account. This is a process that is necessary for the orderly flow and scheduling of workloads. You can imagine the number of requests that have flowed out from concern over Hinsdale, Hugo, and the San Francisco earthquake. These teams are both busy and tough to get hold of. There are from one to seven members on these teams, based on information from around the industry. The time it takes to do the necessary research on a particular customer's request is not insignificant; the recordkeeping between the LEC and the IXC is different, coupled with the impact that divestiture had on the industry. What used to be maintained by one company is now divided into pieces. As if that is not enough, the facilities and networks that we have built are dynamic, not static. Therefore, the information is constantly changing. Keeping all parties up to date is a monumental task.

This is not to imply that the information is not available, or that it is haphazard, but merely a cautionary explanation to the complexities involved in obtaining useable and accurate information.

Most carriers will provide this service either free or at a nominal cost the first time. You will then be requested to maintain it. Should you attempt to get periodic updates from the carrier, as the means of updating your records, there may be a fixed (higher) fee or a time and materials charge passed on to you.

5.4 WORKING WITH YOUR VENDORS

You should also work with your equipment vendors. This will provide a means of comparing your inventory with theirs. A degree of accuracy can be obtained if multiple parties are involved with the inventory. Ask them for their records of:

- Equipment you have on site
- Date of installation (if you do not know it)
- Serial numbers
- Revision numbers of the hardware involved
- Maintenance contracts available and those you have
- Any contractual obligations they may have in support of your systems and hardware

- Availability of spares in your area
- Procedures you should follow during and after a disaster
- Escalation lists for emergencies (on and off hours)
- Costs of replacements
- Systems and services they can provide after a disaster
- Any help they can give you in disaster planning
- Availability of roll-in type replacements

Figure 5.6 is a representation of a roll-in replacement, mounted in a trailer. This is a PBX system which is typically smaller than what you currently use, but will provide degraded service. The trailer will con-

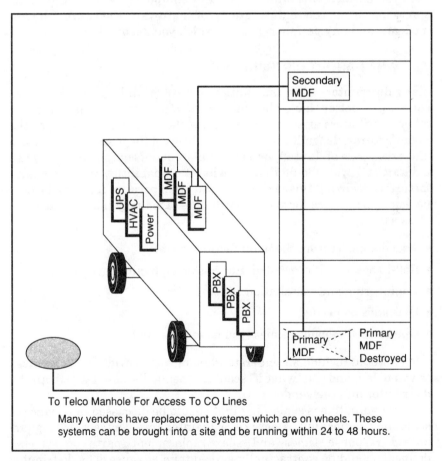

To Telco Manhole For Access To CO Lines

Many vendors have replacement systems which are on wheels. These systems can be brought into a site and be running within 24 to 48 hours.

Figure 5.6 Vendor replacement systems on wheels. The roll-in replacement can get you back in service quickly. The system will be self-sustaining.

tain its own power, protection, air conditioning, and Main Distribution Frame (MDF). The vendor can access your secondary MDF, if available through a window, and the Telco facilities, through the manhole outside the building.

Many system vendors now are providing some form of disaster recovery and restoration planning for their systems and hardware. This will vary depending on the vendor. The range is from complete systems to modified systems, depending on your needs and the capabilities of the vendor involved. It would be prudent that you get as much information up front, before a disaster happens, so that you know what you can expect from the vendor. It is always too late after it happens.

A series of service packages are being offered by the vendors, which will encompass the need for the system, the maintenance and repair of the system, etc. This will include the equipment you have on site, spreading over the entire group of hardware, software, muxes, modems, and any peripheral pieces which you deem critical.

5.5   WHAT ABOUT DISTRIBUTORS?

Many distributors offer capabilities to recover and restore which are equal to, or better than, what the manufacturer offers. Unfortunately, other distributors exist who cannot meet the same service levels as the manufacturer, depending on the capabilities of the distributor, the size and experience of its staff, and the availability of equipment. If you use a distributor, you should find out what its capabilities are. The manufacturers, realizing this is the case, will often arrange for some form of backup type service for their distributors. This may include such services as:

- Added support from the manufacturer's staff
- Roll-in systems if the distributor has no equivalent system
- Engineering and installation support
- Upgrades as needed
- Guaranteed response times (you have to define)

This would include an understanding of who provides what services to you today, and the "what if" scenarios being discussed with both the distributor and the vendor.

Once again, this is something that should be discussed in advance of something happening. A service or maintenance contract, with guaranteed response times and spare/replacement parts or systems defined, should be contractually agreed to in advance. The distributor should also provide lists of key people, escalation procedures, and the manufacturer's contact in the event a disaster strikes.

5.6   ASSESSING YOUR RISK POINTS

Once you have developed the inventory of all components in your systems and mapped out the networks, the next step will be to look for the points which are at greatest risk.

Some of the points that deserve a critical look are:

- Physical security of the facility
- Entrance points from the LEC into the building
- Carrier-to-carrier handoff facilities
- Availability of alternate routes to the carrier(s)
- Environmental conditions in your operation, including the following:

    Electrical

    Fire suppression

    Fire detection

    HVAC

    Water detection

    Training

    Policies and procedures

    Change control management

All of these areas can be exposure or risk points in your environment. You must develop a clear understanding of what is going on in and around your network and facilities. Some added points will be external considerations, such as any construction ongoing in your area, and the effects of weather on your equipment and networks.

You cannot assume that any one of these areas is insignificant, or at less risk than any other.

Why look at all these pieces, when you are only concerned with telecommunications?

To begin with, the telecommunications systems and networks require certain security and physical environments to operate smoothly. Each of the areas that are addressed above will have some impact on your ability to operate and maintain the systems and networks. Additionally, if these areas are ignored, the risk for a disaster is greater. Remember what causes a disaster. There are many factors which can affect your ability to provide service to your organization. The absence of any of these conditions may cause severe outages or extended periods of downtime. Prevention is the rule to apply here. If you can take a serious inventory of the operating environment, and spot weaknesses in the system, you can prevent the disasters caused by both environmental and human elements. This strengthens the environment, so that you can concentrate on the elements that are beyond your internal control.

Thus, it becomes obvious that a host of factors exist that we as telecommunicators must be concerned with before we can feel relatively safe. We can address these individually as follows:

Physical security

Can anyone off the street or within the building gain access to your critical telecommunications, data communications, or networks equipment and facilities? What procedures exist to stop strangers or unauthorized personnel from entering your areas? The result of this survey may well be a shock. Many companies would be mortified if the access to their facilities was truly known. A telephone technician (or anyone posing as one) usually can go anywhere in the buildings unchallenged. Users seeing a telephone technician assume that the technician knows what to do, and belongs there. Unfortunately, this is not always the case, and problems ensue when the wrong person enters the secure/nonsecure facility.

This is one of the easier points to address. Keep all doors locked to your cable vaults, equipment rooms, cable risers, and any IDFs that exist in the area. Maintain a log of who should have access to these locked areas, and who attempts to gain access without permission. Keep all equipment locked, and if there are locks on the PBX, Mux, etc., keep them secured. This prevents unintentional access and deters the curious from causing potential problems. If a security system, such as closed circuit cameras and monitors, is available, install them to prevent access into your operating areas. The data processing departments have been doing this for years, limiting access to only personnel who have a need. We should do the same.

If you are in a highrise tenant building, you should work with your building management to have all IDFs on individual floors secured. Insist on being apprised of who needs access to the areas, and why. You have a right to demand this security of your equipment and services. Oftentimes contractors are allowed into these areas for the purpose of performing some function totally unrelated to your equipment. However, these contractors can cause service interruptions unknowingly. Further, the maintenance personnel in buildings are also given access to areas which they may not be familiar with. Evidence exists in a number of highrise office buildings that the maintenance technicians enter a telecommunications and data communications closet (Intermediate Distribution Frame Room) and proceed to move equipment, without realizing what it is they are moving. The result is a breakdown in the communications flow when connectors are disconnected. One such example in a high-rise occurred as follows:

When the highrise was built, the building management was interested in getting the occupied space ready for the anchor tenant in the building. The construction was behind schedule, so management decided to devote all of its resources to the completion of the tenant space. By doing this, the utility rooms were not completed. These rooms were built to house the tenant's communications and local area network equipment. Yet the back end of these rooms was designated as the electrical closet. Once the tenant began to run the communications cables (consisting of telephone wires, coaxial cables for the LAN, and other alarm circuits), it was necessary to secure the wires to a backboard mounted on the walls. Although this is standard practice, the walls which the backboards were mounted on were not completed. The original plan called for the drywall to be taped and spackled, which had to be postponed due to schedules. The tenant, using a thick wire Ethernet coaxial cable system, coiled the cable in each of these rooms for future growth. The cable system allows for a tap no closer than eight feet apart (an Ethernet system uses a vampire tapping system where a pin penetrates the cable and makes contact with the center conductor). The extra coils were left there for future taps. In order to secure the cable and prevent damage to it, the customary practice is to coil the cable and secure it to the backboards. The cable was secured with a series of u-hooks, holding it tight to the wall.

When the building was finally occupied, the management company decided to finish the work that had been postponed. Thus, a maintenance person was sent to these utility rooms to tape and spackle the joints where the drywall came together. The problems began there. The maintenance person, unaware of the system in place, but chartered with the responsibility to do the taping and spackling, merely assumed it would be alright to pop some of the clips off the cables that were coiled in front of the joints, and bent the cable 180 degrees to clear the joints. The bending radius of the cable is far less than 180 degrees, so a kink occurred in two spots on the cable. This caused a total disruption in the communications flow of the tenant's LAN. A communications wiring technician had to be called in to cut and splice the cable to repair the damage, which was bad enough. However, while this was all going on, the tenant's 1000-plus users had lost their ability to move information and/or share files, printers, etc. This is a disaster!

Unfortunately, this was not the end of the problem. The tenant's Director of MIS made an appeal to the building management to keep these technicians out of the communications rooms, but if it was necessary for them to enter the room, to alert the MIS staff in advance. A member of the MIS staff would accompany the technician into the room as work was being done to prevent further occurrences like this. Of course the building management agreed to do so, but felt that the tenant was limiting its ability to provide the necessary services. Everyone was in agreement on the procedures that would be used for future work, or so they thought.

Two weeks later, the same individual who caused the original problem got into the telecommunications closets and created another set of panic situations for the tenant. Since the taping and spackling still had to be completed, the individual got back into the telephone closets and started to do the work again. This time instead of pulling the cables off the wall, the technician spackled around them. However, while spackling, the trowel (a device used to do the spackling) got clogged with the spackle compound, and needed to be scraped off. The tenant has a communications cabinet in these rooms, which have 19" racks. The side rails on these racks are metal with straight, clean edges. Thus, the technician used the side rails to scrape the spackle off the trowel, which caused globs of this compound to fall down on the electronic equipment mounted in the racks. Once again, the tenant began to have problems with the network, because the compound got into the electronics and shorted and overheated the equipment, causing it to fail. At this point, the tenant finally demanded the building management to do something about the problem of unauthorized access. Management agreed to succumb to the tenant's demands.

Entrance points into your facility
Do you know how and where the LEC gets into your building? Do you know what condition the cable vault is in? Is the cable vault kept locked? These are all additional areas that may be exposed to disruption, yet appear to be beyond your control. Not true. You have a responsibility to your organization to understand the risks to any part of your networks. If the cable vault is left unlocked (although unlikely), you must take the necessary steps to secure it. Additionally, if the telephone company personnel are not keeping the vault clean, uncluttered, and free from fire hazards, you must take action! These areas are usually off limits to customers and users alike. These areas are sacrosanct, considered the domain of the LEC. Unfortunately, many users are intimidated into believing this. However, the area affects your ability to conduct your business, therefore you have a vested interest. Further, company policy by the LEC requires this be designated as a nonsmoking area. The risk of methane gas buildup in a cable vault exists. Check the vault for telltale signs of cigarette ashes, butts, cigar stubs, and pipe tobacco. If it appears that someone is smoking in this area, stop it immediately.

Use smoke detectors, set to a very sensitive adjustment, to alert you if someone is smoking in this area.

Here again, keep the cable vault and entrance points secured. Another point to assess will be whether you have a single entrance point into the building. This creates a single point of failure, where all cables from the LEC are routed into a choke point. A fire, flood, or vandal in this area can seriously impair or disrupt all of your service at this point. Determine if there are any other points of entrance into the building that may have been overlooked. There may be an opportunity to have the LEC bring service into different points, thereby minimizing a total disaster in the event a problem occurs. The points of entrance may be adapted to accommodate additions of telecommunications cables. For example, if the electrical service enters the building from a different point, perhaps you can get access from the electric utility. (Electromagnetic Interference [EMI] may cause some potential problems here. Use due caution when considering this point of entry.)

Another possibility would be the water or sewer entrance points into the building. Many instances have arisen where carriers (particularly alternate access carriers, which will be discussed later) have gained access through the sewer lines, since the other utility companies would not give right of way. Consider the consequences if this route is chosen. Rodents and sewer gas may present other risks to your facilities, not to mention the risk of water in the sewer lines. If you plan to use these as access points, then you must take extraordinary steps to protect the cable. For example, the conduits may be run on the top of the sewer pipe (inside) suspended from J hooks, but must be sealed with a waterproofing material to prevent seepage. Further, the cables must be rodent proofed. Rodent proofing is done through the use of chemicals in the outer cable jacket to deter and/or repel the rodents. An interesting note here: Several studies have been conducted to determine if any particular cable types are better than others. These studies were conducted in open fields with buried cables laid out, with a variety of cable types and colors. The surprising fact is that the rodents had a tendency to leave orange and yellow cables alone. Although no final conclusion has been drawn to answer why this is so, initial analyses are twofold: either there is something in the pigments used to create the colors, or the rodents (like insects) may have a problem with the color spectrum in the orange and yellows. Further studies are under way to draw some conclusions as to why this phenomenon happens. Consider the use of our fiber optics cable routes laid across the country today. All are in an orange colored innerduct. It would appear that some validity exists with this premise regarding the rodent proofing of the cables through color.

Carrier-to-carrier handoff facilities
How does the LEC meet the IXC to hand off your long distance circuits? This involves dedicated and switched services. Determine if
there are alternate routes from the LEC's CO to the IXC's POP. This
takes a little longer to obtain the information, but the time and effort
are well worth it. Standards are being addressed in the telecommunications, data communications, and network fields through the
standards bodies. SONET (Synchronous Optical Network) is a standard that will attempt to address the carrier-to-carrier handoff, and
be responsible for fiber optic systems. This standard is designed to
provide for the demarcation points from the LEC and IXC for a midspan meet of fiber, assigning maintenance and repair responsibilities. SONET will take time to be fully accepted and deployed, so plan
now for whatever options you may have.

Alternate routes to the carriers
One of the most vulnerable points in your network is the local loop
from the LEC to your building. This is not to imply that the LECs are
remiss in their responsibility of delivering quality service to the
door. It is, however, a proven fact that most cuts occur along the local
loop, due to construction in the cities. Secondly, the local loop was
designed for analog transmission facilities years ago. Since that
time, upgrades to digital technology required the replacement of
amplifiers and loading coils with regenerative repeaters every mile
along the route to the CO. These repeaters fail from time to time,
which cause service disruptions. Bridge taps along the analog routes
are also prevalent, which can cause noise, static, etc., thereby causing network impairment. Additionally, the splice points along the
way, vaults, handholes, etc., flood, which can disrupt the local loop.
Other possibilities exist which can occur along this route, any of
which will have some impact on your service. As a means of preventing total failures, the alternative is the use of diverse routes.

Diversity can come in various forms:

1. The first is to stay on the same route, but obtain cable diversity if
   multiple cables exist along the same route.

2. Another possibility is sheath diversity in the same cable route.

3. Still a third is count diversity, the least desirable of all diverse
   routing schemes.

In each of these cases, the diversity is along the same route and/or
conduit, which does not buy you a lot.

4. Another approach is a totally diverse or separate route, which
   oftentimes does not exist. The LEC can design and build a new

route to your door, but the cost will probably be prohibitive. The typical costs industrywide for the construction of a new route is between $80,000 and $250,000. This is handled on an Individual Case Basis (ICB) and will vary by location, LEC, distance, etc. You need to talk to the LEC about this, although most companies who begin this process are usually discouraged with the cost and reluctantly walk away from the project. Keep in mind, you are dealing with limited funds. This type of an expense could totally deplete any budget you have for disaster recovery planning. Use your communications dollars wisely, and get as much accomplished with the limited resources (dollars) you have. Research other technologies to get what you need for diversity. Additional technologies will be discussed in a later chapter.

Environmental conditions
This aspect covers the full gamut of the operating environment. You should be cognizant of the operating characteristics of all your equipment per the manufacturers' specifications. The areas you should be concerned with are many, with the most obvious listed below. These areas are the ones that will be the most likely to create problems, yet there are other possibilities too numerous to list here.

1. Electrical:
   A good many failures of telecommunications systems and networks are caused by electrical problems. There have been studies conducted by AT&T, DataMation, Computerworld, and the research houses. These studies indicate that most of these problems are caused by sags in the voltage levels, resulting in temporary memory outages. This accounts for about 87 percent of the electrical problems. The second area is from impulse noise on the line, followed by total failures and surges, respectively. From a building standpoint, there are a few easily defined steps that can be taken to mitigate the problems caused by power conditions. Most PBXs use a form of battery backup which will help to sustain operation over a period of four to eight hours in the event of a power failure. The commercial power is usually run through a rectifier and through the battery to clean up the power going to the switch. This is not foolproof, but it is a basic step. There are other systems on the market which will clean the power before getting to your system. Oneacs are power filters that can be mounted in front of the switch to filter the sags, spikes, and impulse noises. Not a perfect solution, but it is an improvement. Power conditioners are sold on the market which regulate the voltage into the systems, and will do a lot of the cleanup. These are typically fused so

that any deviation from the acceptable variances will spur a blown fuse. The upper end of the protection arena is an Uninterruptable Power System (UPS). This device can be battery or generator powered and will allow you to sustain operations for a specified period of time and/or power down gracefully. The UPS will help to clean up most of the power problems, such as spikes, surges, sags, brownouts, blackouts, frequency variations, transient noises, impulse hits, etc. This all depends on the type you have. The cost of a UPS can range anywhere from $15,000 to over $150,000, based on the size and configuration. A little investment here is a wise one. A UPS can prevent other problems as well.

2. Fire suppression/fire detection:
   This area is usually a requirement of most of the local zoning ordinances, the National Fire Protection Agency, the National Electrical Code, the local fire marshal, and insurance companies. The use of smoke and heat detectors to alert you in the event of a fire will save time and lives, as well as equipment. However, most people who have these systems either do not realize they have them or how to use them. Learn what you have and how to use it. Then, train your personnel on the use of the equipment. Periodically, check the systems to ensure they are functioning properly. You may be surprised at what you will find. There are a number of systems that have keyed access to shunt them. Inspections reveal that this is a regular practice. Here you have a system that is designed to save lives and equipment, but it is ineffective because it is turned off. Make sure that a company policy is written to prevent this, and then make sure your people are aware of the policy requiring these systems to be left on at all times. Enforce this one strongly. The exposure here is high and the legal consequences can be extremely high if a fire occurs and a life is lost because of human error.

3. HVAC:
   All electronic components are designed to operate in a clean and cool environment. Most computerized systems also like a humidity controlled environment. The use of air conditioning systems in your operation usually will include all of these. However, have you considered what will happen if you lose power? You may be caught off guard in an extended power interruption situation. We go through great pains to protect our systems with battery backup or UPS systems. Yet, the HVAC systems also need power to run the chiller or tower for cooling. When power is interrupted, and the HVAC is down, the room will heat up fast, necessitating a power-down of the telecommunications systems that are up and running.

This is due to a thermal protect switch in computers and communications systems, which, after the room reaches a 95 degree temperature, will start to activate warnings, or the system will begin performing erratically. Keep in mind the need for cooling to prevent a disaster. Computer and communications disasters in the past have resulted from overheating the equipment and forcing it to power off hard. As a result, many of the electronic components can be damaged, causing them to perform intermittently until a total component failure takes place. The result is another disaster, weeks or months after the first one, disrupting the communications flow of the organization.

4. Water detection:
   This is a controversial topic these days. Many of us have had vendors drum into us that there shall be no water pipes in the ceiling (or plenum space) due to the risk of leakage. The leaks that may occur will wreak havoc on communications systems! Yet the fire codes in many cities are now being interpreted to require the use of sprinklers overhead in communications and computer rooms. Thus, it would behoove all to consider the use of a water detection system. The water detection system will go under the raised flooring, and will determine if a problem exists, since you cannot see under the floor on a daily basis. A caution here: Air conditioning systems use a floor drain in most under-floor systems. This is proper, however, and periodically you should check these drains. All too often, these drains are allowed to get plugged up. This may cause sounding of alarms, due to improper maintenance. Further, when checking under the floors, be careful that your employees do not disconnect the detection probes wired under the floor. If you have one, inspect it, or have a qualified company conduct an inspection, to ensure the system is working properly. Cleaning companies, hired to clean under-floor systems, inadvertently disconnect these probes with their vacuum cleaner attachments. Your coverage against water damage will only be as good as the systems provided to protect you.

Looking at the Alternatives

6.1 LOOKING AT THE ALTERNATIVES

What can you do to protect the assets you have in place? One way is to look at all the alternatives. No one can say for sure just how many alternatives fit into each and every site plan. The truest picture you can paint is to research every one available in your area. The use of a detailed approach to protect your organization's well-being cannot be limited to one or two possibilities. Thus, you must consider them all, based on the issues at hand:

- Availability
- Reliability
- Ease of use
- Cost
- Legal or operational constraints

In order to successfully delve into the alternatives, we will concentrate on these in the following areas:

- Technologies available. As already mentioned, the possibilities are numerous.
- The use of alternate access carriers for local access to the IXCs or to

other network points in the same city, etc. Now that the alternate access carriers are colocated in the Bell Telephone Company COs, the opportunities abound.

- Shared services with other users or companies in the same industry or same geographic area.

- Reconfigure or reroute what you have in place with the intent of not "breaking the bank."

- Look at the costs associated with each alternative to prevent excessive spending. Many of the alternatives, since they may be backup capabilities, do not have to be as elaborate or in the same quantities as your primary service.

Once again, there are no pat answers; the decisions on the alternatives to be used are dependent on a site by site, company by company basis.

6.2   TECHNOLOGIES AVAILABLE

A multitude of technologies are available for your use as listed below. The use of these technologies encompasses the operational, environmental, and cost issues you will have to consider. Each of the technologies has both its positive and its negative considerations, the least being, for the purposes of disaster recovery planning, the cost issue. Yet you cannot lose sight that the funding for the project and the available services may be somewhat limited. Some of the alternative technologies are:

- CATV
- Cellular radio
- Fiber optics
- Infrared
- Microwave
- Satellite and VSAT
- Two-way radio

6.3   CABLE TELEVISION (CATV) SYSTEMS

Attention has shifted away from the coaxial systems as a disaster recovery and restoration technique. Coax has been used in telecommunications for years, primarily as a means of interoffice communications by the telephone companies and long distance carrier networks.

However, the coax has been replaced by other technologies (fiber and microwave) which have diminished emphasis on its use. Coax has large amounts of bandwidth, ranging in the 350 to 400 MHz and above arena. This is an analog technology (carrier) which can be channelized to carry multiple inputs for voice, data, or video. Further, a local area network (LAN) operating at four to ten Mbps can be accommodated with channels on this system. Inputs on the coaxial system can be either digital or analog, which should address most of your needs.

Oftentimes a user of telecommunications services gets frustrated with looking for the alternatives, yet overlooks this technology. The bandwidth is impressive, as compared to twisted pair and other systems. The system is complex to manage, including the need to coordinate and manage the frequency allocation and spectrum assignment, but the benefits may well outweigh the complexity.

An additional concern is the need for rights of way to run coax cable. If this technology is planned as a diverse route facility, then the cable has to be run in a route to the LEC or IXC over some right of way. This process could take substantial effort in getting the access to rights of way (if ever obtained), and add a considerable amount of time to the planning process. The cost of installation is not insignificant as a means of alternate routing.

An alternative to providing your own cable would be the use of a commercial CATV, which may already be installed by the local cable TV company. If the following conditions exist, the use of coax may be simplified:

1. The local cable company has cable running by the facility you plan to connect to.

2. The cable system is a two-way system. Since most cable TV systems are designed as one-way transmission of television to the end user, the amplifiers and equipment may be simplex only. Upgrading the system from one-way to two-way can be expensive. This is a negotiable between the user and the CATV company. Many of the CATV companies are considering or installing newer two-way systems for future use.

3. The cable company has available bandwidth, usually called institutional channels, which has been unassigned, or other spare channel capacity reserved for future use. Do not overlook this possibility.

4. The cable passes by the LEC or IXC offices, and the carrier is willing to accept the termination in the office from the CATV company.

5. A mutually acceptable pricing arrangement can be negotiated. This may or may not be reasonably expected.

In the event the LEC or IXC will not allow direct termination of the cable system in their CO, the use of some closet facilities located in a building close to the CO or POP would be a possibility. Terminating the CATV in a rented closet close to the CO or POP and bridging the channels to a twisted pair running next door to the CO would also be an acceptable arrangement. Figure 6.1 is a typical layout of a connection to a CATV system, allowing video conferencing, data communications, and voice communications patching to another CO.

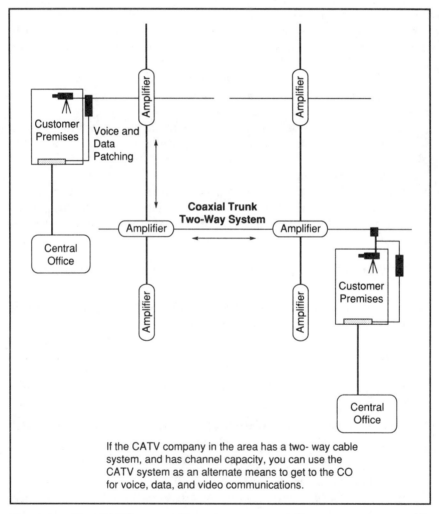

Figure 6.1 Use CATV as an alternate access supplier on a two-way cable system.

6.4 CELLULAR RADIO

Cellular is one of the hottest technologies that exist today. The use of cellular systems was a key ingredient for many of the companies that were involved in the San Francisco earthquake. Since a good amount of the damage to the telecommunications network was the result of cables being broken or pulled out from entrance facilities, cellular has some advantages. The first is of technology. It uses an airborne medium: radio waves. The users of cellular service were able to remain on the air, communicating as normal. The facilities were up and running the whole time. There were some minor inconveniences in using the service, but overall it performed admirably. The cellular companies are very intent on providing the same type of engineering service and design of a CO. They are building redundancy into their networks, have spares available (including towers), provide the same backup power systems (generators, batteries, etc.), and work from a position of providing the most up time available (their targets are for 100 percent, but 99.9 percent may be more realistic). The use of this technology has a couple of risks and drawbacks, though.

The largest risk to an organization is security. No one can truly say that the airwaves are secure. A lot of dialogue has been going on in the industry about security of cellular signals. The signal will travel great distances, even though the devices are low power output (three to five watts and less). The use of a radio scanner (such as a Bear Scanner) allows listening capability on a channel, and in the event of a handoff of the frequency, the same scanner can pick up the conversation on a new frequency. There are groups of people who have a lot of fun listening in on conversations. Security in the type of information passed on a cellular system should be a prime concern. You could go from one type of disaster (natural, physical, etc.) to a different type (breach of security and loss of information) if you are not careful.

The cellular companies have some other risks, which you should be aware of. The first is the risk of losing the Mobile Telephone Switching Office (MTSO). If a disaster occurred, causing the loss of the MTSO, the cellular company would need a diverse route from the cell site to another MTSO. In many cases this does not yet exist. The alternatives that many companies are looking at are to create some intelligent cell sites that could operate as stand-alone sites if the MTSO failed. This requires some investments in the cell sites to include some computer equipment (some indications are that Digital Equipment Corporation Vax 11/780 computers were being considered), but that adds to the vendor's cost. This supersedes the basis of the cell site being inexpensive and its potential ubiquitous positioning if the cost of the cell site now includes enough intelligence to act in a stand-alone mode.

Secondly, the use of frequencies is limited in each cell. There are 45 frequency pairs per site. Therefore, should a disaster strike, the risk of the sites becoming totally congested or blocked is high. From a company perspective, another consideration is the priority restoral system. Although this has not been an issue, if more users begin using cellular as a backup type service, and a major outage occurs in the area, cellular companies can resort to the Telecommunications Priority Restoral Service (TPRS) Plan which calls for national defense agencies, fire, police, hospitals, etc., to get service back before the normal business user. If you put all your eggs in one basket, you could wind up with severely restricted services. Another risk is the possibility of jamming up the cells. If everyone (this assumes a natural disaster) in an area had a loss of physical communications and jumped on the cellular system, then the frequencies would become jammed. Thus, availability would be severely impeded, providing contention with limited returns. The cellular companies are aware of this possibility and are making strides to alleviate the possible problems. Their first approach is to use more cells, and second is to evolve to digital cellular, either Code Division Multiple Access (CDMA) or Time Division Multiple Access (TDMA), which should provide much more channel capacity. CDMA should yield a twenty-fold increase whereas TDMA should yield a fifteen-fold increase in available use of frequencies in the future.

Studies are presently under way to expand the frequencies, and to improve performance of cellular as a technology. Many companies are considering direct digital links from their PBX to a cellular company as an alternate means of communicating from their building. This link can be physical (copper, fiber, etc.) or airborne (microwave or infrared). Additionally, the use of internal cell sites within buildings is drawing more attention. If you have a disaster in a contained space, a building, a floor, or whatever, then cellular may be an alternate way of getting quick communications restored. This is primarily a voice technology today (FAX and data are severely limited), but who knows just what the future holds for us in the area of cellular technology.

Cost is an issue when dealing with cellular. However, when the choices are expense and no communications, expense moves into the background. An awareness of the cost for making and receiving calls (typically $.45 per minute in area and $.75-plus per minute in roam) helps in planning the budget process. There is no real way of predicting the cost on a global scale. However, sticker shock usually sets in when a new user gets the first monthly bill. The technology, although useful, is not without its expense. The future holds the possibility of a reduction of 20 to 30 percent on a cost-per-minute basis, but for now we pay the going rate. The air time rate ($.45 to $.75) for both transmission and reception is added to the cost of the long distance or message unit costs per call. Just be aware of the facts.

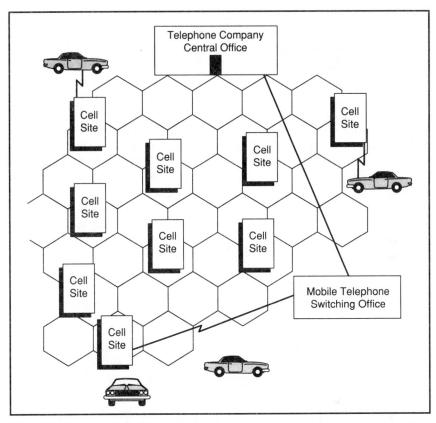

Figure 6.2   The cellular radio/telephone network. The cellular network offers some advantages for users as a backup and alternate technology.

Figure 6.2 is a typical layout of the cellular network with multiple cell sites deployed. The technology uses radio frequencies to patch to a telephone network.

As mentioned earlier, the use of fixed cell sites is now becoming a consideration. A stationary cell site would be installed in a customer's location. The vendor provides all of the necessary coordination with the carriers for the use of frequencies in this area. The system can accommodate up to 90 channels of capacity and can work as an automatic connection to the networks after a cable cut or CO failure. The cell site will be hardwired to trunk ports in a PBX with an alternate routing scheme in the routing tables of the PBX. If the local trunks fail, the cellular links will automatically be used to connect callers.

Cellular has always been considered a voice-only technology, due to the handoff from cell site to cell site. Data communications was considered very limited in its application for cellular. However, recent developments have improved the reliability and the speed (throughput) of these systems. Today's technologies allow data transmission at up to 19.2 Kbps and facsimile at 9.6 Kbps. Another technology being developed is the use of data over/and/under voice via an X.25 packet switching arrangement at 9.6 Kbps in both directions.

6.5 MICROWAVE RADIO

Microwave radio has been around for a long time. At one time it was a phone company technology, but over the years has become a vital link in many companies' networks. The use of microwave can provide another airborne technique to get communications from your sites to the LEC, to an IXC, or to another site (private).

There are a number of reasons private users employ this technology in their networks. Some of the more prevalent have been to:

- Provide large bandwidth capabilities intra-campus and inter-campus
- Span bodies of water and valleys
- Bypass the local operating company facilities
- Provide private networking capabilities

Of these reasons, the bypass arrangement became most popular at the onset of divestiture (the breakup of AT&T from the Bell Operating Companies). However, more users have found this technology useful to provide a diverse route to their IXCs, and to the operating telephone company's facilities.

When dealing with the possibility of providing a diverse route, the use of microwave has a couple of newer possibilities. The first is a means of getting around a single choke point of cable facilities into a building, campus, or other facility. Some of the operating companies have been offering microwave to the customers' premises for quite some time now. It is only recently that more of them are considering this offering on a case-by-case basis. As a user, or as a telephone company, consider this alternative. Telcos can now start offering this as a second path into a customer's premises, on an Individual Case Basis (ICB) in lieu of running a second cable route to the location. The cost of the second cable route as discussed before is anywhere from $80K to $250K-plus. This is not something that a company will jump at because the cost is unrealistic. This is not to imply that the operating company is unrealistically pricing the route construction; it is an expensive proposition and the cost reflects the amount of time and material needed. However, as these Telcos begin rolling in their newer fiber facilities into their networks, the older microwave systems are becoming spared. In many cases the microwave is not fully depreci-

ated, so if they can start renting out channel capacity along a rede-
ployed microwave system, the new revenue stream will help to offset
the costs of depreciating this equipment.

Secondly, when a customer tries to look at microwave, the risk is
that the bypass philosophy will creep into the equation. Rather than
allow the customer base to install and maintain their own facilities,
Telcos are beginning to realize that this is a bypass defense. Many customers have approached their Telcos in the past, requesting an installation of customer-owned microwave in a CO. This is not well received
from the Telco, and justifiably so. Understand the implications of that
request:

1. If everyone went out and bought a private microwave system, and
   installed an end in the CO, there would not be enough room in the
   COs to accommodate the equipment.

2. Customers or their designated service agencies would need access to
   the CO around the clock. Many COs are unmanned, thus access
   would be limited. Additionally, the risk associated with outsiders
   accessing the CO and damaging other networks and equipment
   exists. It would be unrealistic to expect a Telco person to accompany
   every vendor into a CO on a regular basis.

3. In the event of fire, vandalism, natural disasters, etc., the Telcos
   cannot take responsibility for the insurance of the equipment, or the
   liability for the loss on the network.

There are other issues involving the installation of private equipment in COs which can be discussed individually with the LECs.
However, if the demand for this service is increasing as a fail-over for
disasters, the Telcos would be wise to consider this as a service.

In the event the local company will not consider the service as an
alternative, there is always the rusty switch possibility. This, simply
stated, is the rental of a closet, room, or space in a building that is adja-
cent to the CO. Installing the end of a private microwave system in this
rented space and cross connecting to a cable(s) to the CO will give you
the equivalent of a diverse route. This was discussed in the coax scenario above. Unfortunately, this is an unmanned operation which
could cause some delays in restoral if the service should ever fail. Do
not forget backup power if you consider this alternative.

The use of microwave will require certain licensing and path clearance considerations. A path clearance to prevent interference with
other radio users in the area would require frequency coordination,
line of sight between the transmitter and receiver, site layout, FAA
notification of tower construction (for tall towers), as well as other

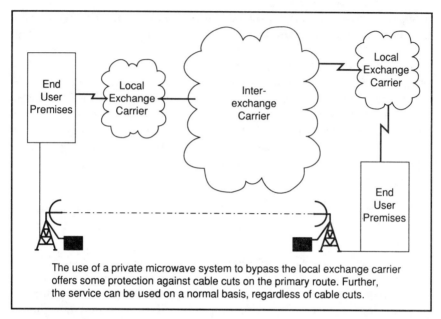

The use of a private microwave system to bypass the local exchange carrier offers some protection against cable cuts on the primary route. Further, the service can be used on a normal basis, regardless of cable cuts.

Figure 6.3   Private microwave. Private networks/switched services. The use of private microwave allows large amounts of bandwidth to connect between customer sites.

issues that would be site specific. Figure 6.3 is a typical layout of a private microwave system as an alternate route to user sites.

Although there is a lot to be said for the use of microwave technology as a means to back up other systems, there are other considerations. First, the tower is susceptible to high winds, tornadoes, hurricanes, and earthquakes. It would not do if your backup system was also destroyed in the event of a natural disaster. However, the use of microwave also gives you the ability to restore your facilities as soon as the event is over, whereas the LEC will have a separate priority list for restoring services. This could leave you in a lurch, unless you have the ability to control your own services and network facilities. Second, there are delays that will creep into the installation of a microwave system. These can be overcome, but you could be looking at a six-to-twelve-month process of selecting the technology and finally being able to use it. You will be required to have an FCC-licensed technician maintain and operate the system. This does not have to be a stumbling block since you can use a service organization to do this for you until you get your own people up to speed. Many digital microwave suppliers/servicers are available as turnkey operations from the vendors. They will provide the site survey, frequency coordination, license, installation, and maintenance for a fee.

Microwave must be an excellent means of communications. Since the common carriers, who had microwave equipment and licenses, have all evolved to fiber optics in their networks, it is interesting to note that they have not released their assigned frequencies for other's use. They have elected to keep the frequencies and use the microwave as a backup system for their fiber networks.

Many of the IECs are now creatively offering colocation of microwave equipment in their POPs. They will allow the end user to terminate their microwave systems in the POP, bypassing the LEC for access to the interexchange network. Some will provide it all: the system, installation, and maintenance. The rates and fees for these services should be coordinated with the IEC offering this service.

6.6   SATELLITE AND VERY SMALL APERTURE TERMINAL (VSAT)

Satellite technology is another form of microwave, using microwave radios pointed into space rather than lined on the earth's curvature. Satellite has also been around for a long time (since the early 1960s) and has come a long way in the availability of providing service to users.

One of the key advantages of satellite is that Line Of Sight (LOS) is easier to obtain with the satellite than to attempt in a congested city environment. The satellite uses high capacity, high bandwidth transponders in the craft itself. The transponders, usually 24 per satellite, have approximately 36 MHz of bandwidth each. This gives a lot of flexibility to the telecommunications network. The normal way a company will integrate the use of satellite into its network is to provide some form of Time Division Multiple Access (TDMA) arrangement, which allows bandwidth on demand. The technology is reliable, proven, and, since geosynchronous paths have been established, available. The cost of using satellite transmissions is a big concern for the mid- to small-sized company. Larger companies can justify more of these technologies than smaller ones. However, the small- to mid-sized company has some salvation. The satellite suppliers can provide access to the satellite through leased lines to a shared hub (earth station). The potential risk here is that the leased line may be the critical link in the event of a natural disaster, cable cut, etc.

At this point, you may have to consider the use of a microwave link to the shared hub, if it is close enough to your facility. Many companies exist for the sole purpose of providing this type of link to the shared hubs, as well as the vendors who provide satellite service. They can help you in the design of circuitry to their facilities. They can also provide lease arrangements for up-link dishes at your site to allow access to the satellite at a reasonable cost per month. It would be wise to research all of these potential scenarios.

Another possibility is the use of Very Small Aperture Terminal (VSAT) equipment. The VSAT capability will give you some capability to access the satellite with limited bandwidth. This would apply for the backup of critical voice and data type circuits, without the high cost of providing total network facilities. The suppliers of satellite service have some very reasonable pricing schemes for this alternative. For example, a VSAT antenna would cost approximately $15 to $20 for the installation per location, and time would be on an as-needed basis. These VSATs can support conversational voice and a range of data communications services (async, SDLC, X.25, HDLC, BSC, sync, DDCMP, etc.).

In many cases these suppliers have arrangements for their own catastrophic backup conditions. They may have a shared service with another supplier, dial access to the up link, or some other means of providing the service. The restoral of their service is contingent upon normal service within 48 hours or better. However, in the event you need the service on a priority basis, they have additional costs for the prioritization of the restoral efforts. Once again, you would have to explore the possibilities with the carrier.

No known failures exist in the use of commercial satellite once placed in orbit. However, the risk of a transponder failure exists. You should check with the vendor to determine their restoral procedures and levels of backup in the event of a transponder failure. Does the vendor lease transponder space from another carrier, or own the space itself? Is all of the available transponder capacity on a single satellite or multiples? What are the normal lead times for the restoral? All questions should be answered before any agreements are reached.

During the aftermath of the San Francisco earthquake, many users of satellite service demanded time available on satellites. Sensing that the disaster would take some time to clean up, they immediately accessed the satellite and held their space on a permanent basis. This bottled up the availability of access for the casual user. The consideration involved in when to use and how much to use comes into play here. If the service is available to you, will you have the capability to gain access during catastrophic situations, or will you be blocked from access because of demand being too great? Once again, you have to make whatever arrangements are in your best interest.

Figure 6.4 is a typical layout of the satellite communications services operating in an equatorial orbit at 22,300 miles above the earth. This allows for what appears to be a stationary repeater in the sky, overcoming the limitations of line of sight for a microwave system.

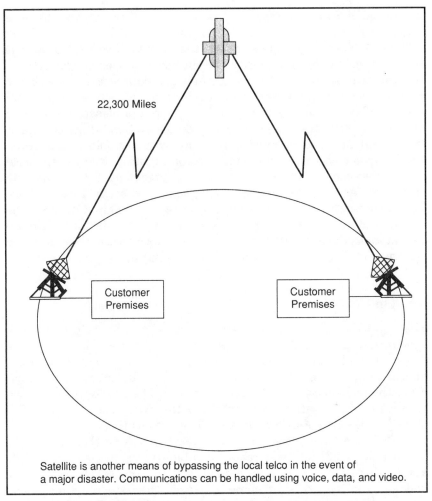

22,300 Miles

Customer Premises

Customer Premises

Satellite is another means of bypassing the local telco in the event of a major disaster. Communications can be handled using voice, data, and video.

Figure 6.4 Satellite communications. The use of satellite communications overcomes the line of sight problems with conventional microwave.

6.7 TWO-WAY RADIO

Two-way radio has some good applications in a disastrous situation, although this technology is often overlooked. The use of two-way radio can provide local communications. The use of this system will allow for some quick communications between team members, between the teams and other agencies (assuming they also have two-way radios on the same frequencies), and, if the service exists, a telephone interconnect. Distance and frequency limitations exist, but the capability to provide quick local communications may well outweigh the distance limitations.

The use of two-way radio requires the user to have the radios, the necessary operating frequencies, the licenses to operate the system, and the trained users. Two-way radio procedures are essential to maintain control and normal protocols in radio telephone usage.

Many of the radio suppliers can assist in the purchase, design, and frequency coordination to provide a workable system for the customer. Additionally, the use of rented two-way radios can supplement the communications recovery process in a disaster situation. Many of the local distributors can provide temporary rental agreements for customers to operate on an emergency basis, using some preassigned frequencies. This should be coordinated with the local vendor well in advance of the actual need to use such a system. Agreements should include the number of radios, the frequencies used, the lead times needed to activate the system, and additional information as necessary.

6.8   FIBER OPTICS

Fiber optics is the technology everyone seems to be welcoming with open arms. The available bandwidth, the potential flexibility, the range of applications available, and the ring topology all carriers appear to be installing lend credibility to the widespread use of fiber. Since the technology is still relatively new in the deployment into private telecommunications networks and the overall use by the LECs and IXCs, the acceptance of the technology is positive.

Most of the IXCs have adopted a ring topology in their networks, because the bandwidth is so readily available to them, they can provide automatic reroute capabilities along the reverse route. This is also the way many of the LECs are going. However, the issue remaining to be addressed is which topology should be deployed. The three basic topologies are the star, ring, and dual counter rotating ring network to deliver bandwidth to the user.

The star network

This is fine as long as a diverse route exists as protection against failure. However, if the star is single threaded, the user and the carrier are at greatest risk to failure. The use of a diverse route tends to drive the costs up for the use of this topology. Therefore, many users will only be concerned with providing a single feed as their primary route for local service, dedicated services, and access to the POPs. The Telcos used a single hubbing, or star, configuration in their environment as

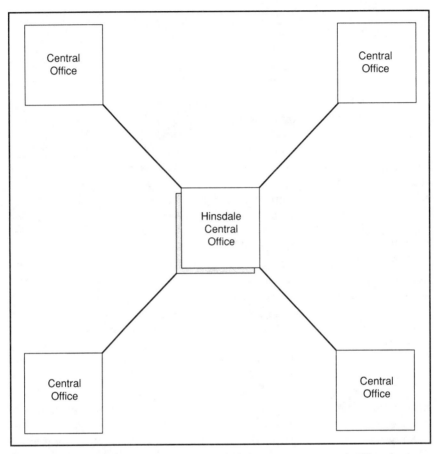

Figure 6.5 Hubbing system in the telephone company network. The star network or single hubbing creates major risks to the network. A single failure will have far-reaching impacts.

an economic decision. Figure 6.5 is a typical layout of a single hubbing or star network environment.

The ring network

Rings automatically provide the diverse route through a single access point. The vendor and user alike gain a lot of advantages using a ring. In the event of a failure of some component along the way, the ring can be reversed to carry traffic in the opposite direction. Many a private user has adopted this technique. The cost is higher, but the risks are minimized. The critical point of failure may well be the entrance to the building, the common cable vault where all the services come together.

Thus, before choosing to deploy fiber rings, a critical look has to be cast on the total route, and choke points eliminated.

The dual counter-rotating ring network

If you could take the best of all worlds, the possibilities become more limited. The Dual Counter-Rotating Ring (DCRR) is the latest and greatest idea in the protection of bandwidth business. If the access into the building can be diverse, and a ring is established with two diverse fiber rings running in two diverse routes to the same location, you have the DCRR. The first ring is installed normally, as any ring might be; the second is run through diverse entrances and along different conduit, pole, or direct buried routes. The most expensive solution to the network configuration, this technique is also the most versatile. Information (voice, data, graphics, images, etc.) are modulated onto both fibers and transmitted to the receiving end simultaneously. The receiver, getting both transmissions, evaluates the information and selects the best signal for use. In the event a problem occurs along the way, causing disruptions to the signal, the receiver will only receive from one source. Therefore the decision to select is null, so the receiver uses the only signal it received. Figure 6.6 is a layout of a ring topology in the network. This particular environment is a DCRR. However, the use of a single ring would look similar.

Fiber optics comes in two flavors: single mode (or monomode) and multimode. Each has its own bandwidth and cost implications. The most common uses of the multimode fiber systems are for customer premises locations, whereas the most common uses for the single mode fiber system are the local exchange and interexchange carrier networks. This determination is arrived at by both bandwidth and economic considerations.

A serious study is under way among many of the research houses, long haul carriers, and universities to determine the impacts of an all-fiber network, using the various topologies outlined above. Expect more information and future developments in this arena in the near future. However, a problem with some of the older fiber optic cables is starting to rear its ugly head. There is industry concern over fiber installed in the Southeast and Northwest several years ago (five to seven) that has since started to cloud (or break down), which will restrict the light from getting through the cable. This can be a forerunner of problems to come. If all the fiber being installed today has short life cycles, then we may have to look for a new technology for the future. The reason is still not fully determined. However, natural phosphates in the ground mixed with water (humidity) may be creating phosphoric acid, which is destructive to glass.

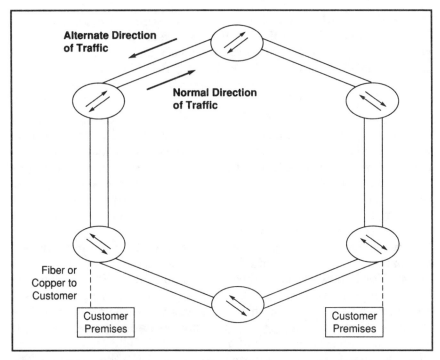

Figure 6.6 Ring architecture using fiber optics in networks. The ring topology being deployed by the Telcos has become a popular arrangement. The bandwidth of fiber optics has made this more feasible.

Additional work is also being done on the automatic recovery of networks. The bandwidth on fiber allows the carriers the luxury of completely protecting their networks. You may remember the disaster we spoke about in Chapter 1 regarding the cable cuts in October 1990 in Illinois. Had the dual fed ring been in place, the problem would have only amounted to a hiccup in the process. Instead, since the fiber ring was not completed, the outages were significant.

Research on an airborne laser technology offers a possible solution to the backhoe fade problem on fiber. Free space optics, a technology being researched, will give us the bandwidth of the fiber over an airborne media. We can expect this to really take off if it becomes commercially available in the near future. Wave division multiplexing (using different colors of light to carry different streams of information) is also gaining a lot of attention in conjunction with the free space optics arena.

Another use, aerial fiber, is now being used in the industry. Fiber cables wrapped in steel strands are replacing the ground wire (or guide wire) for the electrical utilities along their rights of way. The fiber is strong enough, when wrapped in the steel stranded outer jacket, to sustain a hit pole. Extra cable is left along the route to allow for a fallen pole, whereby the cable will not break because it will have enough slack to allow it to fall to the ground unharmed.

6.9 INFRARED

Infrared is a combination technology using an optical transmission without the cable, and the airwaves as its medium. Although this technology is often overlooked, as in the case of coax, there are applications where it fits nicely. The use of infrared, like any airborne system, requires line of sight. Additionally, since the infrared operates in a higher range (100 THz), there are distance limitations and attenuation considerations which must be considered.

Infrared does not require licensing. The distance limitations are approximately one to two miles for the most effective use of the technology. The bandwidth of an infrared system is at the DS2 level (6.312 Mbps). The light is prone to weather fade, particularly in the cases of dense fog, heavy rain, and snow. It is easily transportable, since the equipment is fairly compact. The transmitter and receiver equipment can be mounted inside a building, with the light source passing through a window, providing some protection from the elements. The system is relatively inexpensive, with a typical cost for a system installation of $15–20K.

Once again, the use of this equipment may require the use of a closet in a rented space near the CO or POP, since many of the carriers will reject the direct termination of customer equipment in their offices. Point-to-point services for customer premises equipment on customer locations are also great applications for the use of this technology.

Figure 6.7 is a typical layout of an infrared system for connecting two customer premises together. The system can be used in a point-to-point service for voice, data, and video, as well as alarming and telemetry services.

6.10 ALTERNATE ACCESS CARRIERS

Clearly one of the hottest subjects on the local access scene is the use of alternate access carriers to provide bandwidth directly to the IXCs, bypassing the LECs. There has been quite a bit of consternation by the LECs regarding the alternate exchange carriers coming into major cities and "cream skimming" (that is, stealing away local access facilities from the LEC for only the largest of customers), and not being required to provide services to remote areas, as the LECs are mandated. Obviously, there are two sides to this discussion. The alternate carriers feel they are providing a selected service to their customer

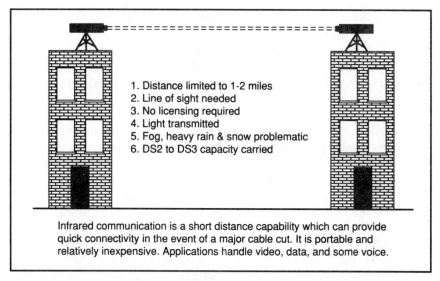

1. Distance limited to 1-2 miles
2. Line of sight needed
3. No licensing required
4. Light transmitted
5. Fog, heavy rain & snow problematic
6. DS2 to DS3 capacity carried

Infrared communication is a short distance capability which can provide quick connectivity in the event of a major cable cut. It is portable and relatively inexpensive. Applications handle video, data, and some voice.

Figure 6.7 Infrared communications. Infrared communications is a quick and easy means of getting connectivity between two customer premises.

base, creating the diverse route that the LECs cannot afford to provide. Secondly, the alternate access providers feel that the customer is the ultimate beneficiary of these services, and room exists for both suppliers to provide ample capacity to each customer, removing the risks in the local plant environment. Figure 6.8 is a layout of how the alternate

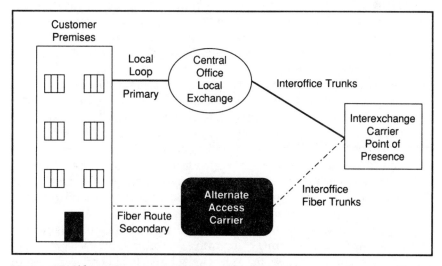

Figure 6.8 Alternate access carriers. Alternate access carriers provide an option to the local customer to gain access to the IEC. This service can also be used for local point to point connections.

route can be run from the IEC to the customer location, through the use of an alternate access vendor/carrier.

Alternate access providers are beginning to spring up in several parts of the country. Some of the activity in this new industry includes the formation of the National Metropolitan Networks (NatMet), which is geared toward providing a single point of contact for establishing the local loop portion of private voice, data, and video circuits. The cities where NatMet will begin offering service initially are New York, Boston, Philadelphia, Baltimore, Richmond, Washington, Chicago, Orlando, Tampa, Miami, Jacksonville, Houston, Los Angeles, and San Francisco. The NatMet is a consortium of four primary vendors today: Eastern Telelogic Corp., Inc. of Philadelphia, Pennsylvania; Institutional Communications Company (ICC) of Washington, D.C.; Intermedia Communications, Inc. (ICI) of Florida; and Teleport Communications Group of New York. This group states, "The association was formed to make it easier for companies to get high quality, high speed, all digital telecommunications services in cities where they either are not satisfied with the current level of service or are simply unaware of the choices available to them."

Another major player in the local access arena is Metropolitan Fiber Systems (MFS) of Chicago. Although not a participating member of the NatMet, MFS is providing service in ten cities around the country today. Pittsburgh, Pennsylvania was recently opened with a network consisting of 144 cables and 855 fiber optic route miles. The MFS Net in Pittsburgh serves approximately 15.5 million square feet of office space in the Golden Triangle. MFS provides digital services ranging from DDS (2.4 to 64 Kbps) to DS3 (672 channels) capacity, based on the customer's need. MFS was a big player in supporting local customers after the Hinsdale fire, providing access to the IECs bypassing the CO.

All of these local access companies provide fiber optic based services within the major targeted cities. Their primary emphasis was to develop rings throughout the cities to prevent the interruption of services through cable cuts, which is so dominant in this industry. A new twist, however, was the challenge to the FCC by MFS to provide local dial tone service to its customers. This is a challenge to break the monopoly that the LEC has on providing service. There will be more to this before the dust settles, but as mentioned earlier the alternate access vendors are now colocating the equipment at the LEC COs. They now can provide alternatives to the local dial tone requirements and carry switched local services.

Another alternate local access arrangement exists, that being the companies around the country providing digital microwave services to local access points. These organizations have backbone services in place using their access to the IXCs, point-to-point dedicated services, and diverse routes to the LECs. Many of these organizations will have arrangements to provide long haul services at the private line to the DS3 level, depending on the customer's needs. One large supplier of this service is a Dallas, Texas based company, QWEST. QWEST was another major player in helping customers reestablish their communications after the Hinsdale fire, supporting local customer's needs.

6.11   SHARED SERVICES WITH OTHER USERS

Another approach to the alternatives available is to consider shared services with other users. The formation of consortiums, where users share the costs for services, is more of an industry specific arrangement, but does not have to be limited to this environment. Major chemical manufacturers, financial institutions, carriers, etc., all have some form of backup and sharing consortiums. These arrangements are typically a form of bandwidth sharing to assist the member companies in the event of a catastrophic loss, although they can also take the form of volume pricing arrangements with the IXCs to provide reduced cost services through the single point of contact. The possibilities are wide, and the eventual reductions in prices are significant. Another version of this consortium is the Mutual Assistance Pact (MAP) where four financial institutions have arranged through an intermediary to provide telephone service to any member who suffers a catastrophic loss of their PBX service. MAP is based in Minneapolis, Minnesota, and was designed as a preliminary step in an overall plan for disaster recovery among four users who shared the same needs and had similar equipment.

An independent offering, the Cooperative Network (CO-NET), provided by a company called National Integrated Systems Services (NISS) headquartered in Maitland, Florida, provides bandwidth sharing for customers of its facilities management services. NISS has arranged volume pricing agreements with network providers to lease bandwidth at the DS3 level, and provide individual channel capacity to its customer base. A single DS0 in this environment could cost considerably less than renting the service from an IEC directly. NISS is also working other arrangements for the recovery of services in conjunction with major carriers.

Figure 6.9 is a mapping arrangement for the NISS network (CO-NET). NISS started out as an outsourcing maintenance organization for customer backbone networks. Evolving CO-NET was a function of serving customers with similar locations and bandwidth needs in various parts of the country. The arrangement between CO-NET users is to share critical bandwidth after a disaster or loss of network facilities. Customers agree in advance to give up pieces of their bandwidth in support of others.

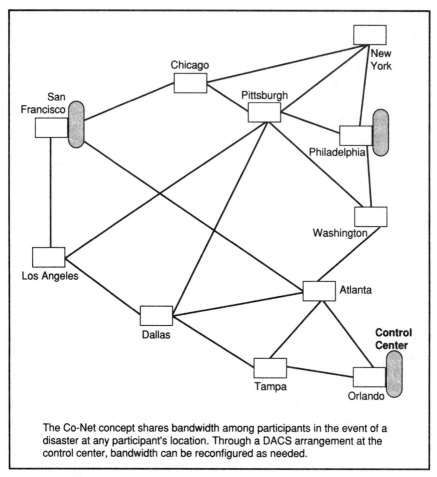

The Co-Net concept shares bandwidth among participants in the event of a disaster at any participant's location. Through a DACS arrangement at the control center, bandwidth can be reconfigured as needed.

Figure 6.9 Sharing network resources through a Cooperative Network (CO-NET). CO-NET allows the vendor to take prearranged pieces of bandwidth to support a customer who has a disaster or network failure.

6.12   RECONFIGURE OR REROUTE WHAT YOU HAVE

The range of possibilities to reconfigure the existing networks currently in use is potentially endless. However, when networks are initially designed and installed, their purpose is within a snapshot in time. Many organizations have recognized that these networks are dynamic (not static) and have continually fine tuned the routing to meet the ever-changing needs of the corporation. The same holds true with disaster prevention and recovery. Any network in existence can be reevaluated for the possibility of a reconfiguration, thereby eliminating choke points and single points of failure, and adding robustness. Through the implementation of the newer service offerings and the subsequent reductions of rates for these services, other scenarios can be considered. Consider, for example, replacing some T1 or T3 circuits with alternate fractional services. Can a T1 be split in half, with each half running through the network in diverse directions, for the same or minor increases in cost? The answer may be a pleasant surprise. The ever-dropping circuit costs for digital services make the possibilities to add robustness especially exciting.

Another possibility may be to split the service between or among various vendors. Have one service routed through carrier A, for example, in one direction, and have carrier B carry the other circuit differently. Then, there is the possibility to put some service on terrestrial services (microwaves) and the other portion on fiber optic routes. Many of the carriers will be more than willing to discuss the possibilities with their customers. As an added range of possibilities consider the satellite carriers to carry a portion of your traffic. With three different technologies on the network, using three topologies, the risks are minimized substantially. This "carrier diversity" must be carefully evaluated before going to others. When using multiple carriers to the same locations, it is important to understand the actual routing of the circuits. No carrier can afford to build 100 percent of all the network facilities they use. As a result, many of the carriers sell or lease off spare capacities to each other, along specific high- or low-density routes. The fiber backbone network will be along the same rights of way, in the same conduit/interducts, or in the same bundle of fiber. If you plan to use carrier diversity, make sure the carriers are not sharing the same routes and fibers (or other technology).

The costs for this diversity of routes may be incrementally higher. Alternatives always exist when dealing with the carriers for bandwidth agreements. These must be prearranged before the final installation. However, if the incremental costs are only a fraction of what a fully redundant and diversely routed circuit might cost, you may well be ahead. The object is to build as must robustness into your network design as possible without breaking the bank. This is only one alternative. Each customer and telecommunications manager has to evaluate his or her own situation.

Figure 6.10 is a typical star network using tail circuits at the DS0 level. The network was originally designed before the introduction of fractional T1 services, but the economics allowed for the installation of a full T1.

Once fractional T1 services became available, the network was revisited and redesigned to accommodate redeployment of the excess capacities. By splitting services, the end points became connected to two different routes, allowing more robustness in the network. Figure 6.11 is the reconfigured network arrangement after the fractional T1 was

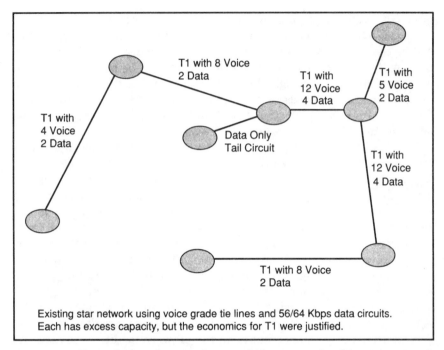

Existing star network using voice grade tie lines and 56/64 Kbps data circuits. Each has excess capacity, but the economics for T1 were justified.

Figure 6.10 Reconfigure what you have: existing networks. The star network was originally built with tail circuits for data communications. The use of T1 was financially justified only to limited locations.

employed. The network rings were designed to minimize risks without major increases in monthly costs.

6.13 USE EXISTING TYPES OF SERVICES

Today's telecommunications networks and facilities are all based on the latest and greatest type of services and technologies. The use of some of the older and more proven technologies still presents opportunities for disaster recovery and restoration. For example, the use of the following are still viable alternatives:

- Use FX and tie lines for diversity. Since FX and tie lines do not get switched at the CO and they only pass through at the wire center, they can be used. In the event of a switch failure (CO type), these circuits will still function. Dial tone for these services will be supplied by the distant CO.

- Switched 56 Kbps service can be used to restore remote processors from a computer backup site. At one time this was an exclusive offering of AT&T. However, the service is now available from multiple carriers, making it both cost effective and efficient. At one

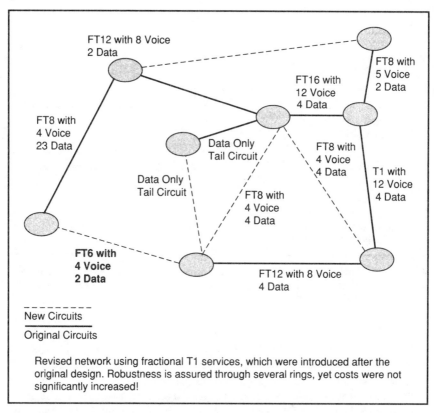

FT12 with 8 Voice
2 Data

FT16 with
12 Voice
4 Data

FT8 with
5 Voice
2 Data

FT8 with
4 Voice
23 Data

Data Only
Tail Circuit

FT8 with
4 Voice
4 Data

T1 with
12 Voice
4 Data

Data Only
Tail Circuit

FT8 with
4 Voice
4 Data

**FT6 with
4 Voice
2 Data**

FT12 with 8 Voice
4 Data

- - - - - - - -
New Circuits
——————
Original Circuits

Revised network using fractional T1 services, which were introduced after the
original design. Robustness is assured through several rings, yet costs were not
significantly increased!

Figure 6.11 Reconfigure what you have: revised network with fractional T1.
Once fractional T1 services became available, the network was reconfigured.
The robustness allowed for more protection using rings in smaller pieces.

time, a fixed charge for the dedicated access line to a switched 56
Kbps service point was necessary, but today that is going away
quickly. It is not universally past tense, but the introduction of all
digital switching from the customer's premises has negated the
need for the dedicated access line (saving from $300 to $500 per
month). Digital Service Units (DSUs) are available with a single
number dialer configuration to provide quick connections after a
circuit fails. Figure 6.12 is a configuration of the DSU with dial
backup capability.

- Use the "rusty switch" or "broom closet" approach to recover your
  network. This implies the rental of a space at or near the CO or POP,
  and the use of passive circuits from this space to the CO or POP. In
  the event of a failure of your primary service, you can use a patch
  panel to connect to the passive system and get back up and running
  quickly.

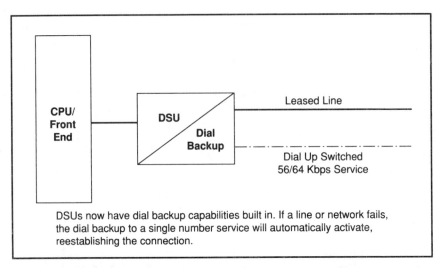

Figure 6.12   Use of 56/64 Kbps dial backup services in the event of a line/network failure. Using a switched 56/64 Kbps backup service will allow reconnection to the location after a line failure.

- Use a T1 local access facility to facilitate both voice and data recovery. The use of digital local loops can provide a significant amount of capability quickly. The T1 local loop placed through a DACS can be diverted to wherever you have prearranged. Figure 6.13 is a typical layout of using a T1 to reroute 24 circuits to an alternate recovery site. It will be much easier to establish a single circuit (multiplexed at 24 circuits) than it will be to establish 24 individual circuits.

- Consider the use of M24/M44 multiplexing as a recovery technique (another version of the above).

6.14   NETWORK HOTSITES

A new phenomenon in the telecommunications arena is the use of a network hotsite. The hotsite or coldsite has been used extensively in the data processing departments for years. Recently, the amount of telecommunications disasters has spurred a new service to allow users to quickly recover at a remote site. This is also the evolution of the digital networking capability, since the major carriers can reroute traffic destined for a single location to almost anywhere. Command rerouting is a service that takes less than 30 minutes these days. AT&T has touted that they have had customers' calls rerouted in less than ten minutes. All well and good if you have someplace to send the calls, such as another owned or leased facility. However, for the larger or smaller

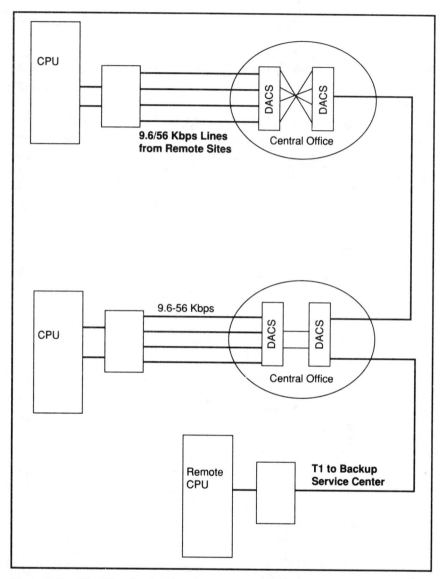

Figure 6.13 Use T1 to backup 9.6/56 Kbps data services. Using a T1 to establish voice and data services provides ease of connection. It is easier to bring up a single circuit.

user who cannot send calls to another of their sites for whatever reason, the network hotsite may be the salvation.

Using switched services, dedicated services, and dialup voice/data capabilities, a customer should be able to restore critical applications in a very short period of time. For example:

- Dedicated 56 Kbps services can be backed up with a switched 56 Kbps service. In the event switched 56 is not available, then a 9.6 to 19.2 Kbps dialup service may suffice. This gets you back in business at a degraded service level. Figure 6.14 shows the use of a V.32 modem operating at 9.6 Kbps, ready to back up the 56 Kbps, DDS service.

- Point-to-point services at any speed can be backed up with dial backup capabilities. The typical operating ranges for data traffic will be over 9.6 Kbps. Figure 6.15 is a modem pooling arrangement supporting multiple lines with dial backup capability. Intelligent modem pools using line sensing equipment can automatically recover a failed circuit over the switched network.

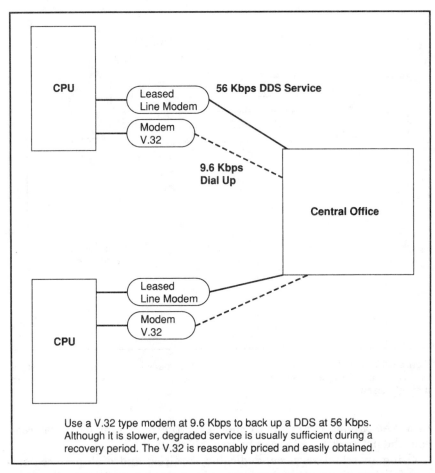

Figure 6.14 Use V.32 modem to back up DDS at 56 Kbps circuit. This will give you degraded services at 9.6 Kbps. However, you will be back in service!

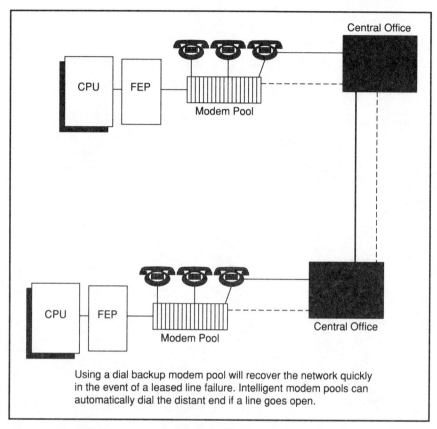

Figure 6.15   Dial backup for DataComm using modem pooling. Using a modem pooling arrangement you can back up multiple lines. Intelligent systems exist to get back into service quickly.

- As Integrated Services Digital Networks (ISDN) begins to proliferate across our networks, the use of on-demand dialup service at speeds of 56-64-384-1536 Kbps will be commonplace. This will avoid the need to provide dedicated facilities for the inevitable disaster. Thus, savings can be achieved, while recovery options will still be accommodated.

7

Vendor and Carrier Strategies

7.1 VENDOR AND CARRIER STRATEGIES

7.1.1 Vendors

With all the emphasis on disaster prevention and recovery and restoration, everyone is getting into the act. This is a good sign, since telecommunications is so critical to the survival of the organization. Plenty of room exists in this industry for many players who wish to enter the arena. Each of the major vendors in the telecommunications and the computer industry is getting involved. The following types getting involved prevail:

- PBX vendors
- Modem and mux vendors
- Computer manufacturers
- Data processing hotsite vendors
- Others
- Carriers

Each of these vendors has some plan in place to assist the customer with disaster recovery options, whereby the customer has some assurances of the vendor's pledge to assist.

7.2 PBX VENDORS

Just about all of the PBX manufacturers in the marketplace have devised some contingency plans to help their customer base. Some of the typical arrangements they are providing are:

Guaranteed response times
Typically two to four hours after a disaster they will have a team prepared to respond to the customer's needs. This is an issue that should be contractually bound when negotiating a purchase or maintenance contract. The purpose of the binding would be to ensure that all parties are aware of the need for instantaneous action, coupled with a written agreement to enact the vendor's team. So long as all parties are aware of what is expected of them, the process will eliminate confusion and finger pointing in times of dire need. The vendors will feel more comfortable with such a document. A word of caution here: this agreement is a clarification of expectations in writing, not a mechanism to pass blame or gain consequential damages for the disaster. Many customers and vendors see contractual documents as wedges to leverage against each other. What you are trying to accomplish is a partnering between you and the vendor who is going to assist you in recovering your business functions.

Roll-in replacements
Many have roll-in PBX replacement systems, which may be less than the customer has working, but are systems to get you back into business as soon as possible. Many of the major suppliers have vans or trailers ready to roll or fly within 24 to 48 hours. The trailer-mounted systems are equipped with many of the necessary amenities, such as: batteries, generators, power conditioning equipment, air conditioning, fire protection and detection systems, etc. It is not prudent to have a replacement system that cannot function independently of the building that has experienced a disaster.

UPS/battery backup systems
Newer requirements demand that systems of certain sizes either be equipped with a battery backup system, or attached to a UPS system. The typical battery backup system will hold the system up for 4 to 8 hours, whereas the UPS system is designed to carry the system for 15 to 30 minutes, to allow for generators to come on, or to allow for the graceful power-down of the system. This means that the system, without a battery backup, will be tied to a timetable consistent with the UPS or with a Mechanical Generator (MG). The generator can be diesel, gas, or natural gas operated.

Remote access to systems for maintenance
This is not new, but the vendor can dial into the system and attempt

a restart, or put cards into/out of service as necessary. Additionally, looking at the system remotely allows an analysis of what parts may be needed, before dispatching a technician or team to the customer's site. Oftentimes these remote access systems are left on around the clock, with a dial-in modem attached. A word of caution here: monitor the usage of this access point into your system to prevent unauthorized access to your system. A hacker who inadvertently (or deliberately for that matter) gains access can cause severe disruptions to your system and network through this access method. Make sure the passwords into the system are sufficient to deter casual access to the heart of your systems. Further, if a vendor's maintenance technician or remote monitoring technician is discharged from the vendor's employ, change the access and the passwords immediately! Make sure the vendor keeps you advised of any adversarial roles in their environment. Several companies have changed the access method by disconnecting the dial-in modem during the normal operation, only to reconnect it when they request the vendor to check the system out.

Still another problem exists which may cause a potential problem using this access method. Installation technicians working at a customer site may find they need additional information for the installation they are currently working on. Knowing that your system is configured to operate similarly to the one they are working on, they may attempt to dial in and scan your system. This can present the opportunity for an error to be introduced. An example of this might be in the route tables for long distance access. A technician may dial in to see how your system is set up. Unknowingly, by prompting the system, they can cause your system to crash, or trip an alarm condition which could lock up your system. Now you have a disruption of your service, which is the result of someone else's mistake. Human error from a remote access! Be aware that this can happen and protect against it. The vendors, of course, will deny that any such activity could happen, but reality states that it can and does.

Automatic dialers
Dialers attached to the system will generate a call to the supplier and alert the supplier or maintenance provider of a problem (power conditions, CPU failures, etc.). Although these are unsophisticated systems, they are effective. Just be sure that the dialer is either self-powered (battery backup inside the box) or connected to the UPS system. It would not do to have your alarming system, which will alert the vendor of power conditions, be unable to generate the call because it is on commercial power which has failed.

Enhanced circuit assurance programs
Circuit assurance software that detects a loss of a circuit and puts the

card out of service, then reroutes traffic over alternate routes, is available in the patterns. This is nothing new, yet the enhancements are far more reliable and will generate the necessary alarms. This will spur action immediately if a circuit fails. With the emphasis on digital connectivity through T1, this method becomes far more critical. If a T1 circuit or digital interface card fails, 24 circuits carrying voice and/or data are affected which should cause more immediacy to the response level. No longer will a single circuit failure be handled casually.

Enhanced power failure transfer systems
Ground start to loop start convertors are included in most installations for emergency dial-out capabilities. Typically, a Gordon Kapes unit will provide 16 to 24 trunks (DOD or two-way) to seize dial tone for outward calling. This applies to lost power. Although not a perfect solution, it does allow for the ability of critical departments/users to make or receive calls. The use of these units has gained a new meaning with the potential power shortages in the industry. An article in a major business publication (May 1989) highlighted the potential shortfalls of power generation to meet the future demands of business over the next decade. Brownouts and blackouts alike may become the norm during peak demand periods, causing potential for loss of communications systems and networks.

Improved power conditioning systems
Typically a power conditioner is provided to clean up the power coming into the system, such as an Oneac unit. An inexpensive unit that provides a lot of protection could well protect the customer from major outages from spikes, transients, and sags in the commercial power. Oftentimes this system is included (or recommended) with the vendor proposal. If not, ask for it.

DC powered systems
More emphasis is placed on using a 48 volt DC source to power systems. Having the commercial 120/208 power run through a rectifier and convertor helps to clean up the power conditions, such as spikes, sags, etc. Further, the vendors will allow for the connection of other devices, such as T1 muxes, through the PBX 48 volt power. This gives you some flexibility in providing added coverage to the mux, since the PBX will have either a UPS or a battery backup system.

Teams assigned to assist the customer
Many of the suppliers have special teams assigned to work with the customer to prevent catastrophic loss of services and equipment. These teams include power engineers, layout designers, business planners, analysts, etc. The major PBX suppliers are all considering the use of emergency planning teams to partner with the customer. This may bear some added cost in some cases, depending upon the

complexities of the individual site and configuration. However, the cost is usually minimal.

7.3 MODEM AND MUX VENDORS

Many of the modem and mux vendors have followed suit with the PBX suppliers, providing emergency replacements for their equipment. This includes the ability to respond within predefined timetables as agreed to with the customer.

Roll-in replacements
Roll-in equipment which can be shipped and delivered within 24 to 48 hours.

Redundancy built in
Redundant critical components (i.e., power supplies, control cards, aggregate cards, etc.) built into the system to prevent down time.

Dial backup capabilities
Many dedicated modems have built-in dial backup capabilities as a standard or inexpensive option. These systems (e.g., 56 Kbps DSUs with switched 56 Kbps) are becoming more inexpensive at an accelerating rate. V.32 modems for 9.6 service are rapidly being deployed as options.

Guaranteed response times
In the event of a disaster, teams are available to respond and get the customer's critical data communications services back in service quickly. Typically this involves response time of two to four hours, but is regularly performed quicker.

7.4 COMPUTER MANUFACTURERS

Just about every major computer vendor has taken action to develop disaster recovery plans to assist the customer with hardware failures and network failures. Each has some form of contingency planning service available to the customer, at a fee. However, the hotsite capability of the computer manufacturers has evolved to accommodate many of the telecommunications services, which is new. Typically, the major suppliers have limited telecommunications services available. Yet IBM's Business Recovery Services (BRS) has gone one step beyond that. They provide the following types of services at their hotsites (which is a different type of service) for their customers:

- Voice dial-up services (approximately 230 two-way lines)
- Modems, muxes, and data switches
- PBX or key systems

- Transportable satellite dishes (12 DS1)
- VSAT capabilities
- T1 and Accunet T1 reserve service (six each)
- Front ends (372x and 374x) (three each)
- Switched 56 Kbps access (eight to 12)
- Spares
- Consulting assistance
- Training

Others have capabilities to assist the customer with analysis of needs and consulting service, as well as software programs to develop the plan, extended or super sets of their maintenance contracts, and fleets of vans with equipment and systems available to roll in. Each vendor does something a little different.

Some of these computer companies are becoming very customer oriented in dealing with multiple platform proposals and joint proposals. An example is where IBM and DEC proposals for disaster recovery and hotsite services are available to end users. DEC will support their equipment at their hotsite, and IBM will do the same. A link between the two hotsites will be required if interconnectivity is necessary.

7.5   DATA PROCESSING HOTSITE VENDORS

The two leading hotsite vendors for data processing services are Comdisco and SunGard. These two organizations control approximately 70 to 80 percent of the market share in this business. Their primary emphasis was to provide hot, warm or coldsite facilities for the data processing departments. However, the increased network disasters, coupled with the awareness of the importance of telecommunications to the organizations, has led to a new development in their service offerings. These companies now offer total networking between their own sites as well as a network hotsite service for clients. The network hotsite will include a variety of services:

- PBXs
- ACDs
- Voice messaging systems
- Pre-wired facilities for phones and terminals
- Dial-up telephone lines
- Modems (1200-19.2 Kbps)
- Digital services (DDS at up to 19.2 Kbps)

- High cap services (56 Kbps-DS1)
- Alternate technologies (microwave, VSAT, infrared)
- Cellular phones
- Muxes, front ends, DACS, data PBX
- SMDR capabilities for call accounting
- Network software services and more. . . .

The press has carried a lot of hype about what these vendors are doing with their networks and services since the Hinsdale fire and San Francisco earthquake. However, Comdisco especially has been touting its CDRS network which is in the process of being implemented. Comdisco has chosen to use the New York Teleport facilities to enhance its network for customer use. All hotsites will be linked together with high capacity digital services, allowing for expanded flexibility for the customer base.

How do these hotsite vendors work?

Each customer who signs up with a hotsite vendor must pay a subscription fee for the privilege of having the hotsite available. The cost of the subscription can range from $500 to $50,000 per month, depending on the complexity of the organization's needs. This subscription guarantees the availability of a hotsite to move into after a disaster. Additionally, a declaration fee is required by some of these vendors to move into the hotsite. This adds to the cost and is a one-time charge that could range from $1000 to $50,000, which makes the hotsite available for a fixed number of days (typically 30 to 45). The cost per day to stay at the hotsite is also a variable, depending on the service arrangements with the vendor. The cost range on a daily basis is approximately $1,000 to $10,000 on a typical user. Some companies charge by the day, others by the hour or the CPU power needed. To stay at the hotsite longer than the prescribed time; to add tests; and equipment/support needs are all extras. Once the customer has used the allotted days at the hotsite, a warm or coldsite can be provided to hold the customer over until full restoration of the original location is completed. The cost for warm and coldsite stays is considerably less expensive.

The selection of a hotsite service provider requires that the customer determine the scope and costs of services provided, the number of subscribers to the service, and the availability of additional sites in other areas. Consider the use of a hotsite that is at least forty to fifty miles away from your location. This prevents the hotsite location from possibly being affected by the same disasters affecting your location.

A newer service, the telecommunications hotsite, or network hub, has evolved since the importance of telecommunications has finally been realized. This service includes the types of equipment listed above, and is generally less expensive. Typical costs for communications hub usage are from 15 to 40 percent of the computer hotsite costs. The vendors are actively improving their capabilities to accommodate the use of hotsites for communications applications.

AT&T has recently announced a service (Protect It), which will be designed around using the freed-up space at their POPs. The POP has all the amenities for recovery and protection, such as:

- Major power systems and backup capabilities
- UPS and battery backup systems
- Access to the long distance network, alternate feeds, and technologies
- HVAC/fire detection/suppression systems
- Raised flooring
- Dual risers/dual entrances into the POP
- Secured vaults for storage
- Space

The Protect It offering can accommodate a department for access to LAN (ring, bus, fiber) as well as sufficient office space to get you back in service as quickly as possible.

7.6 CARRIERS

Each carrier of customer traffic, whether it is voice, data, or image, and whether it is dial-up or dedicated service, has the same concern for the integrity of the network and services they provide. Many of the LECs and IXCs have already started reinforcing their networks. The shoring up of circuits and contingency plans has been actively pursued since the Hinsdale fire in May 1988. Many of the carriers have begun by reinvesting in their own contingency planning efforts for their network. Still some have gone further, where they have developed specific teams to work with customers. These teams specialize in assisting the customer with telecommunications recovery and restoration planning.

7.6.1 LECs

The Bell Operating Companies (BOCs) have begun offering value added services to their customer base through special teams. The BOCs have assigned special teams to work through the account teams in the BOCs to provide information, planning, and consultative assistance to the customer. Many of them are providing this service free of charge. Still others provide service at a nominal fee. The information available to the customer is inventory information, service schematics of the circuit layout (local plant) through the BOC's CO, and general planning for diverse routing.

The LECs have also begun a review of their networks to determine their points of exposure and single points of failure. In order to prevent catastrophic losses on their network, many have begun to design ring topologies into the layout and design of their fiber route. This is the up-and-coming topology, either in a single ring or a dual counter-rotating ring. Those who have not been sufficiently convinced that ring and self-healing intelligence exists have gone to dual hubbing of their COs. Either way, there have been substantial improvements in the overall layout and design of the networks, which allows everyone to benefit. Regardless of the topology, the main ingredient here is the awareness and proactive posture being implemented. Robustness is being installed into their networks with rings and dual homing of services to multiple (two or more) IXC points of presence.

Teams of customers and LECs have begun an interchange of ideas and information. The LECs have been more receptive to the customer input, and the customer has been more confident in the ability of the LEC to provide the service. If this was a global statement, there would be no need to go any further. However, there still exists some hesitation and reluctance to bring all the parties together in pursuit of a common goal. Thus, some customers and LECs have yet to reach a comfort level in working closely together. This is a loss to the industry, the user, and the LEC, as the customer will ultimately seek alternative sources of service and coverage.

A rash of Individual Case Basis (ICB) type services have been provided by the LECs to their customers. These ICBs range from detailed inventories and regular updates to engaging in the installation of diverse cable plant to and from the customer premises to researching alternate technologies for use between the LEC and the customer. An example is the use of microwave on an ICB basis from the CO to customer premises for a nominal fee, or a midspan meet using microwave terminated in the CO and the customer facilities. Both of these instances show progress is being made. Figure 7.1 is a typical layout of a dual feed from the customer premises to two different COs and on to two different POPs.

7.6.2   Interexchange vendors

The primary emphasis of the interexchange vendors has been with the protection of their routes and the diverse routing capabilities for long-haul services. The efforts of AT&T are highlighted here, since they are the dominant force in the market:

Circuit Assurance and Safety Net Services are offerings by AT&T for

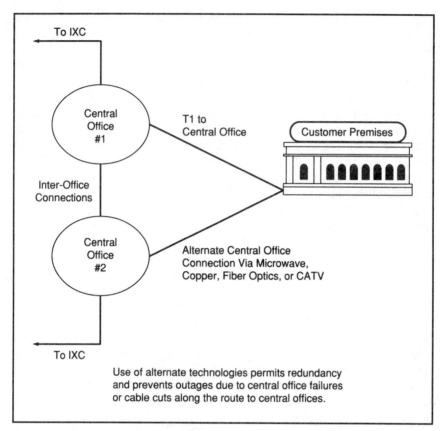

To IXC

Central
Office
#1

T1 to
Central Office

Customer Premises

Inter-Office
Connections

Central
Office
#2

Alternate Central Office
Connection Via Microwave,
Copper, Fiber Optics, or CATV

To IXC

Use of alternate technologies permits redundancy
and prevents outages due to central office failures
or cable cuts along the route to central offices.

Figure 7.1   Diverse routing to IXC through two different Central Offices (COs). The dual feeds from the customer premises to two COs and then to two POPs will prevent major outages in the future.

customers to have a guarantee and comfort level for backing up their networks. However, AT&T is also protecting its network through expanded robustness for interoffice transport. Using high-capacity fiber optics, they are providing protection circuitry which is automatically switched to in the event of a cut. As an alternative, they are now providing the alternate routing via ring architectures employing route diversity rings, dual-fed rings, and reconfigurable rings. A summary of each of these is listed here:

7.6.2.1   Route diversity rings

This is the simplest and most direct way to provide fiber route protection. The primary fiber and the protection fiber run in two diverse routes, with no sharing of manholes, repeater huts, or any other common element. Normally the route is protected on a one by one (1 × 1) basis. This is expensive, since the protection circuit for each working circuit requires a complete system: fiber, repeaters, and electronics. Another technique used is a one by N (1 × N) where N can be 4,5, . . . 10. This allows for some economies, but only a portion of the working circuits are backed up, which can jeopardize the service levels being provided. An offshoot to this is the risk of technical problems using two different routes. The cable will surely be longer on the diverse route, requiring longer cable and additional repeaters. Although this adds to the expense, the greater problem of an unbalanced circuit exists. The fiber systems are designed to a specification and tolerance. The diverse route being different may cause out-of-phase conditions, etc., creating problems for the users. The carriers want the redundancy and quick restoral of diverse routes, but oftentimes cannot justify the expense. Therefore, other alternatives had to be made available.

7.6.2.2 Dual-fed rings

This alternative with a ring diversity switch provides a dual-fed ring topology. The DS3 level signal is duplicated and sent across both loops in the ring. At the receiving location, a switch evaluates the received signal from both directions and selects the better of the two signals to transport to the customer location. If a cut along the primary loop occurs, the signal is immediately available, and the switch at the receiver selects that signal to deliver to the customer.

7.6.2.3 Reconfigurable rings

This technique allows for some economic considerations to be considered. The carrier can build spare capacity into its network for restoration purposes. This technique employs the high-speed cross-connect systems (AT&T DACS III and IV, for example), which allow the carrier to reconfigure the network to provide protection across multiple working spans. This allows more flexibility in the degree of restoration the carrier will deploy and the priority with which the carrier will restore critical services.

7.6.3 Other exchange carriers

Other interexchange carriers are equally concerned with the need to protect the network from critical downtime situations. They are also exploring the use of rings and diversity in their route, and the exposure on their rights of way. Diversity implies two distinct paths in two separate conduits or rights of way. Unfortunately, this is not always the way it works. Many carriers use many different diversity techniques.

To review the various ways, you can look at diversity. A summary is listed:

7.6.3.1   Cable diversity

Service to a given carrier or customer is run in two different cables, yet may be in the same conduit.

7.6.3.2   Bundle diversity

The customer's service is provided in different pairs, in different bundles, and in the same sheath.

7.6.3.3   Count diversity

The customer is given a count of one hundred pairs in the same cable.

7.6.3.4   Right of way diversity

The customer's service is provided in two different cables in two different rights of way.

7.6.3.5   Adjacency diversity

The customer's service is provided in two different cables, yet in the same right of way, and usually the same conduit.

7.6.3.6   Adjacent innerduct

Customer's service is separated into different cables in the same conduit (or innerduct system), but in different innerducts.

With all the emphasis on the cable cut situations, possible threats of vandalism, and threats of train derailments along rights of way, the network is exposed. There has to be a better way to protect the nation's cabling system from disruptions.

7.6.4   When is a diverse route not a diverse route?

Many customers unknowingly think they have diversity in their routes and therefore are well protected. However, the interexchange carriers cannot afford the diversity that customers are looking for. As a result, the carriers share rights of way, share cable facilities, and trade off bandwidth to each other in certain routes. This exposes the user and the carrier to a lot of mistrust and argumentative situations.

Additionally, some users (customers) believe that by spreading their services among multiple carriers they get diversity. This is not always true. The carriers using the bandwidth trading along certain routes may well have the customer's service from two carriers running in the same cable. Think of the day when the service is interrupted and the customer experiences network outages from both carriers at the same time. This is not the time to find out that the diversity in the network is only one of billing, rather than of facilities. The carriers are now reacting to intense user pressure to get more diversity into their networks. More users are demanding schematic layouts of their circuits and detailed maps of whose cable facilities the circuits run through.

7.6.5 Independents

The independent telephone companies are also in the midst of reviewing their networks and the possibilities available to them. They have different regulatory and funding issues to deal with, but are continually monitoring the market for the latest developments. Many of the independents have begun deploying a diverse route over ring topologies, while others have stayed with a dual homing system with cable facilities.

Networks and Topologies

8.1 TOPOLOGIES AND NETWORKS

The various telecommunications processes and networks must be protected and recovered quickly should a disaster strike. It would be prudent to review each network and topology used in your organization. Remember, only critical applications and services are to be provided during the recovery period. Some of the topologies and networks you should consider are:

8.1.1 Local area networks

Whether they are in the form of a ring, bus, star, tree, or token-bus, many of these are becoming critical to the end users' ability to perform their jobs.

8.1.2 Wide area networks

The connection of similar or dissimilar networks together across a country, region, or globe. Each of these may carry significant impacts to the business if they cease to operate.

8.1.3 Metropolitan area networks

The connectivity and operation of a network within a major metropolitan area, such as a citywide network. More emphasis is now being directed toward these because of the bandwidth being utilized.

8.1.4   Electronic tandem network (ETN)/
Electronic switched network (ESN)

Primarily a voice dial-up connection (limited data) for the routing of calls across a private or hybrid network. However, its loss may impact the operation substantially.

8.2   LOCAL AREA NETWORKS (LANs)

8.2.1   Media

These networks are fast becoming the replacement vehicle for the transport of information within the organization. Moreover, the networks are being exposed to a multitude of risks. In the beginning stages of deployment of LANs within companies, the use was based on a departmental need, and used only for the largest of companies. Today, however, the use of LANs has virtually displaced the use of many mainframe applications and has proliferated into the smallest of organizations. From the small business with a handful of devices to the largest of corporations, this technology has rapidly spread, bringing with it the risks associated with a single topology. The media used are as follows:

- Coaxial cable (the first type of LAN used this media almost extensively). The coaxial systems can be either baseband or broadband.

- Twisted pair of copper, which, depending on the system and the building used, can be shielded or unshielded.

- Fiber optics cable, a newer system which is quickly gaining in popularity of installation. Fiber was originally used as a transport mechanism for the carriers. Now, it is the cable of choice for many organizations in their intrabuilding distribution.

- Infrared or wireless, which has been around for years. A new application for the wireless system is in the LAN arena. Many organizations are experimenting with the deployment of this capability, particularly because of its transportability.

8.2.2   Equipment

Each network involves far more components than the simple wiring configurations above.

- The wires must be terminated into a device, requiring an interface from the cable to the device. This tap or jack or connector is something that is a consideration. How the cable and the device interface often dictates the flexibility and the costs associated with the connection.

- Once the connector is selected, the Network Interface Card (NIC), which front ends the terminal, printer, file server, etc., must be considered.

- Cable runs are limited, depending on the topology and the media used. The use of other components, such as repeaters, amplifiers, sort haul modems, etc., is to be reviewed.

- Server equipment, which allows many users to share limited resources, including printers, files, disks, modem pools, faxes, etc., cannot be ignored.

- The Data Terminal Equipment (DTE), or the end user device, is the most commonly accessed and abused. This device cannot get away from human interference: smoke from the office, water, soda and coffee spills, etc. However, since it is the most exposed, it is also the most easily recognized and fixed when troubles occur.

- Another set of equipment exists in the closets where the common equipment resides. This is the area where the wires come together and are plugged into the MAUs, Terminal Servers, or other components of the network. Since these are usually hidden from view, they are both less exposed and more exposed at the same time. Less exposure exists since the closets should be locked, thereby limiting access to these devices. More exposure exists since they are out of sight, and no one will notice when alarms, lights, or external forces are at work. This also includes the exposure from contractors, maintenance personnel, etc., who are not familiar with the sensitivity of the components.

8.3   METROPOLITAN AREA NETWORKS (MANs)

These networks involve the extension of the in-house network to other facilities within a geographical boundary of a city or a major metropolitan area. The distances on these networks are usually greater; therefore, the problems can be increasingly more complex. The main reason for this complexity is the involvement of others, such as:

- Local Exchange Carriers
- Alternate Access Carriers
- Interexchange Carriers

The bandwidths used on these MANs are significantly higher than that of the individual LANs. Thus, the impact of outages is heavier.

8.3.1   Media

The primary media of choice in MANs is geared toward fiber optics. The use of a single thread or route from customer premise to premise is the least expensive proposition. Therefore, these are dependent on the offerings of the carriers and the topologies available in a given area. Once again, this technology is exposed to the risk of the external environment, such as rodent damage, cable cuts, flooding in the conduit systems, and the dangers of humans in and around the cables running underground.

8.3.2   Equipment

The fiber optics system used today does not allow for in-line repeaters or regenerators. Instead, the use of repeater huts or equipment along the route must:

- Take the photonic signal (light) back to a digital signal (electric) and
- Regenerate it back into a light source.

This introduces the potential for additional errors or outages due to the numbers of regenerators and the external construction environment. The current technology allows for the fiber to be repeated approximately every 20 to 30 miles for single mode fiber, and every five to ten kilometers (four to six miles) for multimode fiber. Each step along the way introduces greater complexity. Once in the cable vault at the customer's premises, the fiber hubs or fiber muxes are also components that can create downtime. This equipment can fail. The use of redundant components and critical circuitry is necessary to prevent major problems. Unfortunately, the added redundancy introduces more costs. The first question to answer is the degree or the criticality of the information you are trying to protect.

Connectors to the fiber system are varied, and the costs associated with them are equally variable. From the fiber to the customer's environment, there may be additional panels or racks of equipment which have the same exposure as the LANs within the building. Further, the use of a bridge or a gateway to allow connectivity onto the fiber MAN introduces new components that are of concern.

8.4   WIDE AREA NETWORKS (WANs)

Leaving the home state and city to connect to other premises, the concept of a WAN is the connection of multiple sites and networks to act as a single entity. The use of shared resources, such as:

- a processor
- a high-speed print server
- a communications gateway

all benefit the end user. However, if the shared resource is a critical application or a single point of access, the network becomes far more critical. Two thoughts reign in the use of the WAN arena.

- First, there will be no single entity that would bring individual LANs or MANs to a halt. This implies that in order for each LAN or MAN to operate, the components will have to be duplicated at each point. This can be an expensive proposition and takes away from the general concept of the WAN.

- The second thought is that in order to derive maximum benefit from the WAN, single points or services will exist on the network. A host processor, for example, would not be duplicated on the network because of the cost. Therefore, if the connections to the remote sites are impaired, access to the host would be limited for the duration of an outage.

How then would access be gained, if the host is destroyed?

8.4.1 Media

The primary media used in a WAN is dependent on the carriers involved, or the organizations' ability to provide other services. The long distance nature of a WAN implies that a fiber backbone from an Interexchange Carrier will be used. The Local Exchange Carrier may be using twisted pair cabling to get from the CO to the customer premises at each end.

However, other technologies may well be used. Microwave radio systems can carry the bandwidth necessary for the connections to the IXC (bypassing the LEC). Infrared can perform similar functions. Copper can be used, but a cable television system (broadband coaxial cable with two-way transmission capability) is an alternative. Satellite and VSAT capabilities can provide sufficient bandwidth in most cases, leaving options for this connectivity. The private components and networks built around or within an organization can provide multiple options.

8.4.2 Equipment

Additional components will be introduced to the WAN over the LAN and the MAN. The use of combination repeaters for the media will be inserted onto the network. Further, routers and bridges can be used to provide the connectivity. Newer versions of bridges and routers combine both functions into what are called brouters. Lastly, the use of the gateway may also be included into the WAN, particularly if dissimilar networks or protocols are used at various locations.

8.5   BANDWIDTHS

The bandwidths associated with these networks vary. The individual network, operating system, topology, and media all have a bearing on the ability to move information. For the most part, many of these networks are geared toward carrying data, video, or CAD/CAM type information across the network. Thus, the ability to move the information depends on the applications being supported and the equipment and media used. Table 8.1 is a summary of the network, topologies, and capacities typically used.

The topologies dictate the bandwidths being employed above. However, the media is not limited to the systems listed above. Table 8.2 is a summary of the bandwidth of the various media being used today. This is not a defacto limit of the bandwidth, but rather a summary of the typical bandwidths.

With all this bandwidth on our Local, Metropolitan, and Wide Area Networks, you can see that the costs and the downtime costs would be substantial.

8.6   OTHER NETWORKS (ETN/ESN)

Many organizations have proliferated their voice and low-speed data communications across the dial-up telephone networks. The use of hybrids exist in many of these, with portions of the network owned by the company and the rest being leased or rented from the carriers. Depending on the traffic and the financial considerations, the networks use the best routing capabilities available at the time of the call.

TABLE 8.1 Summary of Network, Topologies, and Capacities		
LANs	Rings	4 or 16 Mbps
LANs	Bus	10-20 Mbps
LANs	Tree	200 Mbps
MANs	Rings	100-150 Mbps
WANs	Star/ring	9.6-2.048 Mbps

TABLE 8.2 Summary of Bandwidths of the Various Media Being Used		
Twisted pair	Unshielded	* up to 20 Mbps
Twisted pair	Shielded	* up to 20 Mbps
Coaxial	Baseband	up to 20 Mbps
Coaxial	Broadband	up to 400 Mbps
Fiber	Multimode	up to 565 Mbps
Fiber	Monomode	up to 2.48 Gbps today, but 13.9 Gbps in future

* Today's technology now is based on 100 MBPS in an FDDI network over twisted pair wiring.

8.6.1   Media

Since these types of networks are designed around a dial-up connection, the media is primarily what takes the place of the offerings of the carriers. The use of twisted (unshielded) pair wire, or fiber optics from the customer premises to the LEC, then across the interexchange network, prevails. Thus, the media is dependent on the network configuration. Others have implemented their own access to the IEC, through microwave, satellite, and infrared. These networks operate at whatever media is consistent with their financial considerations.

8.6.2   Equipment

Consistent with this type of network is the introduction of the routing mechanism.

- This is typically the organization's Private Branch Exchange (PBX) which stores and forwards the call across the least costly route available at the time of the call.

- Some organizations may have low-cost routing switches (such as a roadrunner or an infoswitch), which stand outside the PBX. These devices are critical to the routing, queuing, and billing within the organization.

- A T1/T3 Multiplexor may also reside in these networks, front ending the PBX or the LCRS. This allows for flexible routing across fiber or copper, and allows the customer to dynamically allocate or reallocate bandwidth as necessary.

- Network processors or customer-owned Digital Access Cross Connect Systems (DACS) may be substituted for the devices listed above. All the size and routing decisions are based on the size of the network, size of the organization, and the financial status of both.

The addition of all these components underscores the protection and the redundancy issues. Although the cost of these devices in both hardware and software are significant, the impact of the business must be considered before ruling in or out any redundancy.

8.7   RISKS

The risks associated with any of these networks have been covered throughout this document. However, the exposures are great. To lose one's network will cause severe hardships on the organization. Some of the risks associated with the networks are the same for the other networks in our world, such as the telephone company exposures, the interexchange carrier networks, etc. The primary points are:

- Human error, which could be as simple as a dropped device.
- Carelessness, which could be inattentiveness when connecting or disconnecting devices on the network.
- Smoking, which could destroy a hard disk from the particles of smoke, or which could lead to a fire.
- Human intervention, such as the inexperienced technician or the maintenance person who disrupts the network inadvertently.
- Intentional harm from a disgruntled employee.
- Penetration from hackers who can wreak havoc on the network.
- Damage caused from tripping over a cable.
- Virus, which can be introduced by employees attempting to load unofficial or unauthorized software, games, etc.
- Electrical spikes, surges, brownouts, etc., which can damage the network components.
- Water damage from sprinklers, overflowing restroom facilities, condensation from air conditioners, etc.
- Cable cuts on the external environment.
- Programming errors from the system programmers, administrators, etc.
- Timebombs set to destroy the programs and data from a hacker or a disgruntled programmer.
- Trap doors left by the vendor to gain access, which is also prone to penetration by others causing security breaches.

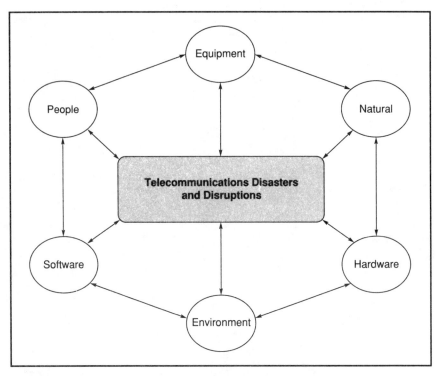

Figure 8.1 Telecommunications disasters and disruptions causes. The disruptive causes to our telecommunications networks and facilities are many, yet most are controllable.

- Access through modem pools or dial access from unauthorized persons. This can be in the form of espionage.
- Inexperience of a user on the network who does not understand the procedures of logon and logoff.

Figure 8.1 is a graphic representation of the disruptive causes to our telecommunications facilities and networks. These are primarily controllable resources, which indicates that if corrective action were taken today, future network disasters may be minimized or eliminated.

The list can go on, but the gist of the information should have you legitimately concerned. The cost of network downtime and penetrations can be in the thousands to hundreds of thousands of dollars per hour. Since these are becoming the wave of the future, do what is necessary to protect them now! Do not wait for the inevitable disaster to strike before building in protection mechanisms, policies, and procedures. It may be too late.

The Plan: Tying It All Together

Most plans, when developed, are treated as confidential or proprietary; therefore, it is difficult to work with a real plan. However, the use of a shell will hopefully help in the planning process. Before beginning to develop the plan, remember to consider the first phase, "prevention." It is far more beneficial to prevent a disaster than to recover from one. Thus, whatever you can do on a preventative scale will be that much less of a concern. However, we all face the risk of having to deal with a disaster. Therefore, if a plan exists which is well thought out and tested properly, the recovery and restoration should be easier. The areas we covered should help, but each plan and organization is unique. There is no boiler plate that will work for every purpose. The following shell is designed to assist in your plan development. Figure 9.1 is a graphic representation of what we are trying to accomplish. From the point in time when an event occurs, until the restoration is completed, and a lessons-learned exercise can be implemented, the sequence may vary from organization to organization. However, the major steps are what we are looking to accomplish.

9.1 DISASTER RECOVERY AND RESTORATION PLAN

The plan is only as good as the effort behind it. Estimates show that approximately 80 percent of the plans in existence today have been

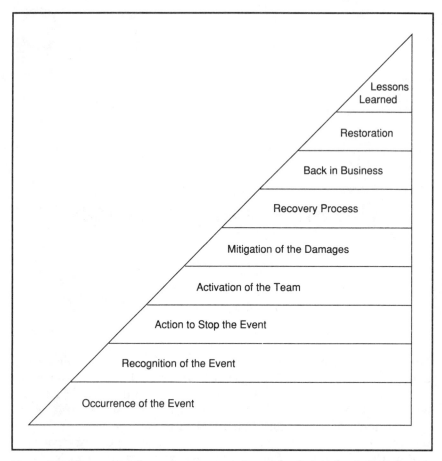

Lessons Learned

Restoration

Back in Business

Recovery Process

Mitigation of the Damages

Activation of the Team

Action to Stop the Event

Recognition of the Event

Occurrence of the Event

Figure 9.1 Sequence of events necessary to get back into business after an event/disaster occurs. The events are listed as a guideline to get back into business quickly. The sequence may vary, but the content should be the same.

written as the direct result of an audit. However, many have never been tested! What good is a plan that has been written and never tested? Better to have saved the time and money than to have a false sense of security. If a real disaster strikes one of the organizations with an untested plan, the results may be devastating. As a result, it would be easy to say that the easy part is done, and the real work begins with the developing, testing, maintaining, and ongoing perpetuation of the "living breathing document," known as the disaster recovery plan, or business continuation plan, etc.

The format below is only a model, but it may help individual organizations to build out from here. In some cases it will fit fine; in others, it will require modifications to match a particular set of circumstances. The budgetary constraints fall within the individual circumstances.

Remember, the planning process cannot "break the bank," or else the plan will be in jeopardy.

Disaster Recovery Plan Outline

Section I.   Administrative statement

Section II.   Action plan policies and procedures

Section III. Testing

Section IV.   Maintenance of the plan

Section V.   Training

Section VI.   Appendices

9.2   SECTION I: ADMINISTRATIVE STATEMENT

This section will be the policy statement for the organization's disaster recovery plan. The main issues to be addressed are the following:

- *Purpose:* To institute a company-wide disaster recovery plan which will protect the organization from catastrophic losses. A statement of what you are trying to protect. This will include:

  A. Definition of the project, what you are trying to do

  B. Determination of what is at stake

  C. The business impact analysis

  D. Definition of prevention strategies to be used

  E. Identification of critical applications

  F. Identification of how much loss can be sustained

  G. Definition of recovery strategies

- *Objectives:* What are you trying to accomplish? This requires an understanding of the company's plans and strategies for the present and future, both on a strategic and tactical level. The planning process will do no good if your plan is going in one direction while the organization's plans are going in a different direction. Make sure that the plan is consistent with the overall direction of the company.

  A. Protect human life

  B. Minimize loss and risk to the company

  C. Maximize recovery and the return to normalcy

  D. Protect the company from legal ramifications/suits

  E. Maintain competitive position

F. Preserve customer confidence and goodwill

9.3   SECTION II: THE ACTION PLAN

This section will outline the policies and procedures to be followed in case an event occurs which jeopardizes the ability of the organization to perform its mission. The areas addressed will be:

- *Policies:* A statement of the purpose and scope of the disaster recovery and restoration plan. This would typically outline the formation of the teams, the actions to be taken after an event occurs, and the critical applications and personnel involved.

   A. Purpose of the policy

   B. The policy itself

   C. Scope of the organization's involvement

   D. Affected departments and personnel

   E. References to other policies and company statements

   F. Definitions of responsibilities

   G. Job descriptions for teams/members

- *Procedures:* The actual action to be taken after event detection. This will cover the various types of emergencies or events that have been outlined in the plan.

   A. Event detection/recognition that a problem exists

   B. Types of events or emergencies
      1. Hardware failure
      2. Software failure
      3. Telecommunications network failure
      4. Building/facilities failure
      5. Fire
      6. Flood
      7. Earthquake
      8. Tornado
      9. Hurricane
      10. Sabotage/vandalism
      11. Bomb threat
      12. Cable cut
      13. Power loss
      14. Security breach
      15. Other as needed

   C. Damage assessment

D. Action to be taken
   1. Protect life
   2. Notify fire, police, medical, management
   3. Determine the nature and cause of the disaster
   4. Minimize the effects of disaster where possible
   5. Inform vendors, employees
   6. Decide to declare disaster (who?)

E. Recovery/business resumption
   1. Activate disaster teams
   2. Activate backup procedures
   3. Relocate to network hotsite (if applicable)
   4. Coordinate with management, authorities, etc.
   5. Notify customers, clients, financial lenders, and media
   6. Reroute network facilities
   7. Reestablish connectivity and facilities
   8. Track work for audit purposes
   9. Maintain systems and facilities security
   10. Begin the cleanup effort
   11. Assess liability
   12. Begin preparation of statements

F. Migration and restoration procedures
   1. Reconstruct site
   2. Restore hardware systems
   3. Restore software systems
   4. Restore power and UPS
   5. Replace detection and suppression systems
   6. Secure area
   7. Rewire facility
   8. Restore network facilities and technologies
   9. Test new hardware/software
   10. Train operations personnel on new equipment
   11. Train/retrain employees on new systems
   12. Clean up area
   13. Schedule migration back to site
   14. Keep management, employees, and media informed
   15. Recognize extraordinary achievements
   16. Coordinate return to normalcy
   17. Prepare final review and activity report

9.4   SECTION III: TESTING

This section will outline the testing of the plan, the policies and procedures to be followed, the purpose and scope of the testing, and the frequency of the tests to be conducted.

- *Policies:* The policies to be adhered to ensure that the plan is tested frequently and that continual updates to the organizational operations and technologies are updated and tested as they occur.

  A. Purpose of the policy

  B. The policy itself

  C. Scope

  D. Affected departments

  E. Responsibilities

  F. Reference documents

  G. Definitions

- *Procedures:* The procedures to be followed in the testing of the plan, so that effective results can be achieved. The plan should be tested regularly, with the intent of seeing *what fails*. If the plan is smooth and nothing goes wrong, then the test is probably inadequate.

  A. Frequency

  B. Pre-test coordination

  C. Scheduled tests

  D. Unscheduled tests

  E. Flexibility

  F. Introduce complications

  G. Evaluate results

  H. Verify all team member activities

  I. Adjust as necessary

9.5   SECTION IV: MAINTENANCE

This section deals with the revisions, updates, and maintenance of the plan. Once developed, the plan should be a "living, breathing entity," which is under constant review and updates. If the maintenance falls short, the plan will be ineffective and obsolete.

- *Policy:* This is the policy statement of the maintenance of the plan which will ensure the constant review and update to the sections that undergo change.

  A. Purpose of the policy

  B. The policy itself

  C. Scope

  D. Departments affected

E. Referenced documents

F. Responsibilities

- *Procedures:* There are maintenance conditions and update procedures to be adhered to.

A. Hardware changes

B. Software changes

C. Application changes

D. Staff changes/team member changes

E. Vendor updates

F. New technologies

G. Contract renewals

H. Vital record changes

I. Forms

J. Emergency assistance changes

9.6   SECTION V: TRAINING

This section will deal with the policies and procedures for training the organization's employees, managers, vendors, and emergency response personnel. The frequency of training and retraining, the degree of information needed, and the methodology used will all be covered.

- *Policies:* Policies are to be used in the formation of the training plan, the degree of information to be provided, and the elements of specialization and generalization to be used.

A. Purpose of the training policy

B. The policy itself

C. Scope

D. Departments affected and involved

E. Referenced documents, if any

F. Definitions and responsibilities

- *Procedures:* The procedures to be adhered to for the smooth and orderly training process of existing and new employees. This will also include training of vendors and emergency response teams (fire, police, medical, etc.).

A. Frequency

B. Required vs. optional

C. Media to be used

D. Generalized training

E. Specialty team training

F. Management team training

G. Vendor and carrier training

H. Distribution and updates

I. New employees

J. New technology implementation training

9.7   SECTION VI: APPENDICES

This section will detail a comprehensive list of appendices to be used. The appendices should be indexed and cross-referenced, the use of graphics and flow charts should be encouraged wherever possible, and the lists should be maintained to be as current as possible. This is the inventory of people, equipment, applications, etc.

Appendix 1: Team member duties and responsibilities

Appendix 2: Emergency call lists of teams, managers, and authorities

Appendix 3: Inventory and report forms

Appendix 4: Test forms and questionnaires

Appendix 5: Maintenance forms

Appendix 6: Applications lists

Appendix 7: Hardware lists and serial numbers

Appendix 8: Software lists and license numbers

Appendix 9: Vendor call lists and escalation lists

Appendix 10: Carrier call lists and escalation lists

Appendix 11: Network configuration and schematics

Appendix 12: Floor layouts of building(s)

Appendix 13: Employee inventory

Appendix 14: Contracts and maintenance agreements

Appendix 15: Operating instructions for equipment and systems

Appendix 16: Cellular telephone lists and agreements

Appendix 17: As needed

Alternate Site Vendors

(PARTIAL LIST)

AT&T
Crisis Management Services
20 Independence Blvd.
Room 1B25
Warren, NJ 07059
1-800-447-0012

Warren, NJ
Off-site storage locations:
Westchester, NY
Southern NJ
Orlando, MD

Agway Data Services
PO Box 4862
Syracuse, NY 13221-4862
(315) 449-6594

Syracuse, NY

Assured Data Corporation
4261 Diplomacy Drive
Columbus, OH 43228
(614) 771-6068

Columbus, OH

Backup Recovery Services
1620 NW Gage Boulevard
Topeka, KS 66618
(913) 232-0368
(913) 233-6862 (FAX)

Topeka, KS

Cadre Inc.   Avon, CT
19 Ensign Drive
Avon, CT 06001
(203) 674-1285

Comdisco Disaster   Carlstadt, NJ
   Recovery Services Inc.   North Bergen, NJ
6111 N. River Road   Wood Dale, IL
Rosemont, IL 60018   Grand Prairie, TX
(718) 518-5681   San Ramon, CA
                                        Cypress, CA
                                        Business Recovery Facilities:
                                        Manhattan, NY
                                        Bridgeport, NJ
                                        Atlanta, GA
                                        Chesapeake, MD
                                        Boston, MA
                                        Columbia, SC
                                        St. Louis, MO
                                        Cleveland, OH
                                        Minneapolis, MN
                                        Indianapolis, IN
                                        Vancouver, BC
                                        Montreal, Canada

Computer Engineering   Moorestown, NJ
   Associates   Baltimore, MD
3922 Vero Road
Baltimore, MD 21227
(301) 247-5244
(301) 247-5407 (FAX)

Computer Recovery   Scottsdale, AZ
   Services
15475 N. Greenway
Hayden Loop Road
Scottsdale, AZ 85260
(602) 443-2588
(602) 998-4628 (FAX)

Computer Solutions, Inc.   Orange, NJ
397 Park Avenue   Clark, NJ
Orange, NJ 07050
(201) 672-6000

Data Assurance Corp.
12503 E. Euclid, Suite 250
Englewood, CO 80111
(303) 792-5544
1-800-654-1689

Englewood, CO
Bridgeport, NJ

Dataguard Recovery Svcs.
PO Box 37144
Louisville, KY 40233-7144
(502) 325-3977
1-800-325-3977

Louisville, KY

**Data Processing
   Security, Inc.**
200 East Loop 820
Forth Worth, TX 76112
(817) 457-9400

Fort Worth, TX
Birmingham, AL
Honolulu, HI
Tulsa, OK

Digital Equipment Corp.
150 Flanders Road
Westboro, MA 01581
1-800-HOTSITE

Parsippany, NJ
Arlington Heights, IL
Business Recovery Centers:
Alpharetta, GA
Bellevue, WA
Burlington, MA
Phoenix, AZ
Cherry Hill, NJ
Englewood, CA
Culver City, CA
Sacramento, CA
Dallas, TX
Detroit, MI
St. Louis, MO

ECC Inc.
PO Box 12707
Shawnee Mission, KS 66212
(913) 681-3661

Kansas City, MO

**Econocom Contingency
   Services**
4400 S. Mendenhall, Suite 8
Memphis, TN 38115
(901) 367-1105

Memphis, TN

Exchange Resources, Inc.   Minneapolis, MN
5700 Green Circle Drive   New York, NY
Minneapolis, MN 55364
(612) 933-6340

First Recovery, Inc.   Troy, NC
PO Box 552
Troy, NC 27371
(919) 576-0901
1-800-548-9377 ext. 241

Hardwood   Chattanooga, TN
  International Corp.
100 Northshore Office Park
Chattanooga, TN 37343
(615) 870-5500

Hotsite   Cary, NC
2000 Warren Avenue   Niles, OH
Niles, OH 44446-1148   Tewksbury, MA
(216) 652-9624

IBM Corporation   Franklin Lakes, NJ
Systems Services Division   Tampa, FL
National Service Division   Detroit, MI
Franklin Lakes, NJ 07417   Atlanta, GA
(201) 848-4243   Washington, DC
                                                Los Angeles, CA
                                                Philadelphia, PA
                                                Chicago, IL
                                                Gaithersburg, MD
                                                Dallas, TX

LDI-Disaster Recovery   Cleveland, OH
30700 Carter Street   Cincinnati, OH
Solon, OH 44139   Detroit, MI
(216) 248-0991   Lakeland, FL

Metropolitan Emergency   Chicago, IL
  Disaster Services (MEDS)
2500 W. Roosevelt Road
Chicago, IL 60608
(312) 226-6337

**Mobile Computer
  Recovery**
211 College Road E.
Princeton, NJ 08540
(609) 452-8980

Princeton, NJ

**National Dataguard
  Technologies**
7000 S. Edgerton Drive
Brecksville, OH 44141
1-800-433-0339
In Ohio (216) 526-8700

Brecksville, OH

NCR Corporation
Disaster Recovery Services
1700 S. Patterson Blvd.
SDC-3
Dayton, OH 45479
1-800-626-3495

Dayton, OH

**Newtrend Disaster
  Recovery Services**
2600 Technology Drive
Orlando, FL 32804
(408) 297-0870

Orlando, FL
Apopka, FL
Maryland

Off-Site, Inc.
32 Ellicott St.
Batavia, NY 14020
(716) 343-9775

Batavia, NY

Prime Computer Inc.
8480 E. Orchard Road,
S-6600
Englewood, CO 80111
(303) 770-0180

Englewood, CO
Durham, NH
Atlanta, GA
Liberty Corner, NJ
Chicago, IL

**Provident Recovery
  Systems**
2000 Regency Parkway,
Suite 255
Cary, NC 27511
(919) 481-0011
(919) 460-7635 (FAX)

Cary, NC
Niles, OH

Recovery Resources, Inc.   Orlando, FL
PO Box 2646
Orlando, FL 32802
(407) 851-7657

SITA Disaster Recovery   Atlanta, GA
3100 Cumberland Circle
Suite 200
Atlanta, GA 30339
(404) 850-5253

Sun Data, Inc.   Philadelphia, PA
1300 Oakbrook Drive   Northbrook, IL
Norcross, GA 30091   Rancho Bernardo, CA
(404) 449-6116   Norcross, GA
1-800-241-9882

Sungard Recovery   Atlanta, GA
  Services, Inc.   Chicago, IL
1285 Drummers Lane   Philadelphia, PA
Wayne, PA 19087   San Diego, CA
1-800-247-7832   Toronto, Canada
          Warminster, PA

Systematics, Inc.   Little Rock #1
4001 Rodney Parham Road   Little Rock #2
Little Rock, AR 72212-2496
(501) 220-5554

Telehouse International   Manhattan, NY
  Corporation of America   Staten Island, NY
1 World Trade Center
Suite 8407
New York, NY 10048
(212) 912-1855

**Upsite Disaster
Recovery Center**
3381 Successful Way
Dayton, OH 45414
(513) 237-3400

Dayton, OH

**Uptime Disaster
Recovery, Inc.**
643 West Stadium Lane
Sacramento, CA 95834
(916) 648-1282

Dayton, OH

Wang Disaster Services
One Industrial Avenue
Lowell, MA 01851
(508) 967-2690

Lowell, MA
Torrance, CA

Western-Southern Life
400 Broadway
Cincinnati, OH 45202
(513) 629-1710

Cincinnati, OH

**Weyerhaeuser Recovery
Services**
Park Center Two PC2-15
Tacoma, WA 98477
1-800-654-9347

Seattle, WA
Phoenix, AZ
Philadelphia, PA

XL/Datacomp, Inc.
908 North Elm
Hinsdale, IL 60521
1-800-323-3289

Anaheim, CA
Atlanta, GA
Bridgeport, NJ
Chicago, IL
Columbia, MD
Irving, TX
Kansas City, KS
Roseland, NJ
San Francisco, CA

Uninterrupted Power System Vendors

(PARTIAL LIST)

Abacus Controls
80 Readington Rd.
Somerville, NJ 08876
(201) 526-6010

Best Power Technology
Rd. 1, Hwy. 80 South
Necedah, WI 54646
(608) 565-7200

Clary
320 W. Clary Ave.
San Gabriel, CA 01776
(818) 287-6111

Controlled Power Company
1955 Stephenson Highway
Troy, MI 48083
1-800-521-4792

Elgar
9250 Brown Dear Rd.
San Diego, CA 92121
1-800-733-5427

Exide Electronics
8521 Six Fork Rd.
Raleigh, NC 27615
1-800-554-3448

International Power Machines
2975 Miller Park North
Garland, TX 75042
In Texas (214) 272-8000
1-800-527-1208

Liebert
1050 Dearborn Drive
Columbus, OH 43229
(614) 888-0246

Nova Electric
100 School Street
Bergenfield, NJ 07621
(201) 385-0500

**Square "D" Co./
Topaz Power Div.**
9192 Topaz Way
San Diego, CA 92123
(619) 279-0831

Satellite and Very Small Aperture Terminal (VSAT) Vendors

AV-DATA Systems
55 Marietta Street
Atlanta, GA 30303
(404) 523-2848

Computer Power
661 Riverside Ave., Suite 110 E.
Jacksonville, FL 32204
(904) 350-1400

Contel ASC
Rockville, MD
(301) 251-8453

Cylix Communications
800 Ridge Lake Blvd.
Memphis, TN 38120
(901) 761-1177

GTE Spacenet Corp.
1700 Old Meadow Rd.
McLean, VA 22102
(703) 848-1000

Hughes Network Systems
1717 Exploration Lane
Germantown, MD 20876
(301) 428-5500

Scientific-Atlanta Inc.
420 N. Wickham Rd.
Melbourne, FL 32935
(407) 255-3000

Pittsburgh International Teleport
PO Box 14070
Pittsburgh, PA 15239
1-800-634-6530

Nova-Net Communications, Inc.
58 Inverness Drive
Englewood, CO 80112
(303) 799-0990

Racal-Milgo Sky Networks
2050 Charlotte Plaza
201 S. College St.
Charlotte, NC 28244
(704) 377-2232

AT&T-Tridom Div.
840 Franklin Court
Marietta, GA 30067
(404) 426-4261

Satellite Technology Management
3530 Highland Avenue
Costa Mesa, CA 92626
(714) 557-2400

Canadian Satellite Communications, Inc.
Mississauqua, Ontario
Canada
(416) 272-4960

CNCP Telecommunications
Toronto, Ontario
Canada
(416) 232-6760

Telesat
Glouster, Ontario
Canada
(613) 748-0123

Disaster Recovery Planning Software Vendors

(PARTIAL LIST)

Information Management Technology (IMT)
Product:
  Total Business Recovery
  System (TBRS)
(206) 823-0441

CHI/COR Information Management, Inc.
Product:
  Total Recovery Planning
  System
1-800-448-8777

Comdisco Disaster Recovery Services, Inc.
Product:
  Compas
(312) 698-3000

System & Business Solutions, Inc.
Product:
  Continue-The Disaster
  Recovery Solution
(215) 296-9080

Strohl Systems
Products:
  Multilevel Planning System
  Single Site Planning System
  DRP-EZ
1-800-634-2016

Executive Compumetrics, Inc.
Product:
  Corporate Recovery
(312) 687-1150

EDP Security
Product:
   Disaster Plan 90
(508) 486-8080

Parnassus, Inc.
Product:
   Coseco
1-800-225-8024

Profile Analysis Corp.
Products:
   Recoverpac
   Recoverpac II
   Riskpac
   Federal Riskpac
(203) 431-8720

Target Marketing Group
Products:
   DP-AID-2001
   DP-AID
(314) 487-2734

Disaster Recovery Related Magazines

THE FOLLOWING ARE MAGAZINES SPECIALIZING IN DISASTER RECOVERY ISSUES:

Contingency Journal
PO Box 551628
Dallas, TX 75355-9987
(214) 343-3717
Cost: $24.00/Annual

Crisis Magazine
PO Box 1111
Dublin, OH 43017-9912
1-800-828-6585
Cost: $30.00/Annual

Disaster Recovery Journal
2712 Meramar Drive
St. Louis, MO 63129
(314) 846-1001
Cost is free to qualified professionals.

Glossary

alternate routing   A feature of most Private Branch Exchanges (PBXs) which sends calls over a different route or line in the event of congestion or line failure. Consider it a process of using other lines, which must be in existence.

arrestor   A device used to protect telephone equipment from lightning and electrical spikes. An arrestor is typically a carbon block or gas tube. After lightning strikes, the gas ionizes and causes a low resistance to ground, thereby draining the surge away from the equipment.

automatic call distributor   A communications system which sequences the incoming calls to a group of agents on an even basis. The system allows for usable statistics to be gathered regarding the hold times, average number of rings, number of agents needed, etc.

automatic recovery   A feature of PBXs to automatically reload the instructions or system programs after a power failure. The instructions are supposed to reload in minutes.

backbone closet   The closet in a building where the backbone cable is terminated and cross-connected to the horizontal or vertical distribution cables.

backup   A copy of computer or communications data on an external storage medium, such as a floppy or a tape. Computers and telephone systems experience glitches, thereby causing them to lose information. Backups save time in returning to normalcy after a failure or loss of data.

battery   Storage systems used in Central Offices (COs) and PBXs which cannot tolerate power outages. They supply emergency power for a limited time in the event of a commercial power failure. Typically, in a PBX world, the batteries will allow for four to eight hours of operation.

broom closet   Using a rented closet or room in a building near the CO to allow for another means of connecting to the CO from the customer premises.

bug   An indescribable glitch that affects proper operation of a system. Also referred to as an unwritten feature, which exists in poorly written software.

bypass   Using a method of local communications other than the Local Exchange Carrier (LEC), either because the local telephone company is too expensive, or they cannot give you the bandwidth, routes, or service you want. This is a bad word to the LECs.

cable   Different types of wires or groups of wires capable of carrying voice, data, and image traffic.

cable bays   Lots of cables arranged like bays in a harbor. Typically a term used to describe the amount of wires you will find in a CO.

cable riser   Cable running vertically in a multi-story building.

cable vault   Room under the main distribution frame in a CO or customer premises, and a prime target for the spontaneous outbreak of fire. It is usually not protected by Halon or other suppression systems, yet the buildup of methane gas is very possible in these areas.

callback modems   Modems that are designed to call you back at a predetermined location. A form of security to prevent people from dialing directly into your network by requiring a password.

carbon block   A device used to protect cabling and systems from lightning strikes. The carbon block consists of two electrodes spaced so that any voltage above the design level is arced from line to ground. They are effective, but can be destroyed if high voltage is directly applied.

cellular radio   Newer radio technology which divides geographical areas into smaller "cells." This system allows for the reuse of the same frequencies separated by different cells.

cold site   Empty shell offered by a disaster recovery company, or provided by the user, into which a complete telecommunications system or computer system can be moved.

conduit   A piping system used to carry telecommunications and electrical cables. A conduit protects the cable and prevents burning cable from spreading flames or smoke. Most fire codes are requiring conduit in highrise office buildings wherever the cable passes through human space, or plenums to return air to human space.

dial backup   A network scheme using dial-up telephone lines as a temporary replacement for failed leased data lines.

Digital Access Cross Connect System (DACS)   A method of digitally cross-connecting circuits rather than using physical wire frame connections.

disaster   The failure of a critical system, network, or power in your telecommunications environment.

diverse routing   Having more than a single physical link between two points. Preferably three different paths between points A and B, depending on the economics. Diverse routing is the physical connection, as opposed to alternate routing, which is the process of using the diverse routes.

emergency dialing   A variation of speed calling that uses preprogrammed buttons to dial emergency numbers (fire, police, etc.) in the event of alarms. Typically found as a button on an electronic telephone.

encryption   The ciphering of data (or voice) by applying an algorithm to plain text in order to convert it to cipher or secured text.

facility   In telephone terms, it is the phone or data line. In business terms, it can also mean the physical plants, structures, or buildings on a campus, either high- or lowrise.

fading   The reduction in signal intensity of one or all components of a radio signal.

fractional T1   A newer service provided by the carriers which allows the customer to take from one to twenty-three channels of digital transmission from a T1 service.

ground   A problem that exists when a circuit is accidentally crossed with a grounded conductor. A wire designed to carry voltages (i.e., lightning strikes) away from electrical and electronic components which may be damaged by the surge. Improper grounding is probably the most significant contributor to telephone system problems!

ground loop   This occurs when a circuit is grounded at one or more points, and can cause telecommunications system problems.

hacker   A person who "hacks" away at a computer or telecommunications system until he or she gets into the programming or features.

hot site   A site fully equipped with a telecommunications system or computer facility, ready to go with a short-term notice. Full environments and systems are in place, and the customer merely moves his people in and begins working.

hot standby   Backup equipment that is kept running (usually in parallel) in case some equipment fails. The hot standby then takes over, since it has been constantly updated.

IDF   Intermediate Distribution Frame.

independent telephone company   A telephone company not affiliated with the Bell Operating telephone companies. There are about 1,400 of these around the country. These independents are also the LECs in their respective areas.

infrared   Portion of the electromagnetic spectrum used for fiber optic transmission and short haul through air, voice, and data transmission.

infrared scanning   A process using infrared technology to detect hot spots in electrical circuits. It has been used effectively to detect problems before a fire or major outage can occur.

Interexchange Carrier (IXC)   The long-distance telephone companies who carry traffic (voice, data, and video) across their networks.

Local Area Network (LAN)   Short distance network used to connect terminals, computers, and peripherals under some standard form.

Local Exchange Carrier (LEC)   The new term to describe the local phone company, whether a Bell Operating company or an independent which provides local phone service.

line of sight   A clear unobstructed line between two communications sites, used typically for microwave, infrared, or other through the air transmission systems.

local loop   The physical wires that run from the customer's premises equipment to the CO. The point at which most failures occur due to construction, cuts, old cabling, flooding in the tubes, etc.

Mean Time Between Failures (MTBF)   Average time a manufacturer estimates before a failure occurs.

Mean Time To Repair (MTTR)   Vendor's estimated average time to fix a problem.

Metropolitan Area Network (MAN)   A network that extends to an approximate 50-kilometer range, and operates at speeds from 100 to 150 Mbps.

plenum cable   Fluoropolymer insulated and jacketed cables with fully color-coded insulated copper conductors. Also called Teflon cabling, which has been designed as a low-smoke-producing cable.

polyvinyl chloride (PVC)   A thermoplastic material composed of polymers of vinyl chloride. A tough water and flame resistant insulator.

power failure transfer   A telephone system feature that allows certain telephones to work when the commercial power has failed and the customer does not have a battery or UPS system as backup.

proactive   Taking the initiative and doing something before someone forces you to do it.

redundancy   Having one or more backup systems available in case of failure of the main system.

restore   Typically means to put a telecommunications system back into full operation after a disaster.

RFI   Radio Frequency Interference.

switched 56 Kbps   A service offering from the carriers allowing the customer to dial up communications (primarily data) at speeds of 56,000 bits per second.

T1   A digital transmission technique that multiplexes 24 channels of voice or data (at speeds of 64 Kbps) across a single four-wire circuit. It is the base level of the digital hierarchy.

Uninterruptable Power Supply (UPS)   An auxiliary power unit for telecommunications systems that provides continuous power in the event of a commercial power failure. Typically it is a bank of batteries, but can also consist of a generator (gas, diesel, or natural gas fired). However, most commercial power failures are of five minutes or less.

warm site   Something in between a hot and cold site. Typically some limited systems and capabilities exist.

Wide Area Network (WAN)   A network which links metropolitan, campus, or local area networks across greater distances. Usually linked together by common carrier lines.

Index

Alternate Access, 90-92
Alternate Technologies, 74
Automatic Call Distribution (ACD), 31
AT&T, 3, 17-18
Alternate Routing, 68, 79

Bypass, 80
Backup, Dial, 100
Battery, 69, 104
Broom Closet, 97
Business Impact, 27-28, 31

Cooperative Network (Co-Net), 93
Cable Vault, 59, 66
Cellular, 77-80
Cold-Site, 17, 109-110
CATV, 74-76
CO, 57, 96
Cable Cuts, 3

DACS, 58, 123
Diversity, 68, 112, 114
Dual Ring, 113
Data Processing Hot Site, 108
Disaster, 1, 6, 125
Distributor, 62
DS-3, 93
DISA, 4

EMI, 67
ETN/ESN, 122-124

Fractional T1, 95
FX, 96
Fiber, 52, 86
Toll Fraud, 4
Fire Detection/Supression, 70

Ground, 52

Hacker, 4
Hot-Site, 17, 109-110
Hurricane, 2, 114
Hinsdale, 2, 11-13
HVAC, 53, 63, 70-71

Infrared, 51, 90
Independent, 115
IMT, 36
Illinois, Bell, 18
Insurance, 34
ISDN, 101

Local Area Networks, 65, 117-119
Legal, 9, 33

MAN, 119-120
Microwave, 80-83
Modem, 51
MUX, 51, 123
MDF, 31, 62
Media, 51

Network Hot-Sites, 98-99

Options, 35, 36
ONEACS, 69

PVC, 13
Penn Mutual, 16-17

Riser, 55-56
Recovery, 6
Recovery Coodinator, 38
Radio, 51
Ring, 87-88
Roll-in, 104

Switched, 56, 96-97
San Francisco Earthquake, 3, 15
SS7

Steering Committee, 25
Secondary MDF, 61
Sonet, 68

T1, 95, 98
Two-Way Radio, 85

UPS, 53, 70, 104

VSAT, 51, 88
V.32 (Modem), 100
Voice Mail, 32

WAN, 120-122
Warm-Site, 110
Wiring, 51
Water Detection, 71

ABOUT THE AUTHOR

Regis J. (Bud) Bates has over 24 years of experience in telecommunications and management information systems. He is the president of Technology Consulting (Phoenix, Arizona), which specializes in the integration of telecommunications and computer systems. Bates develops and teaches both public and in-house professional seminars in telecommunications, and regularly contributes his expertise in research and technical publishing activities. He currently conducts seminars dealing with disaster recovery for telecommunications around the country.